Decision-Making in
Air Pollution Control

PRAEGER SPECIAL STUDIES IN
U.S. ECONOMIC AND SOCIAL DEVELOPMENT

Decision-Making in Air Pollution Control

A REVIEW OF THEORY AND PRACTICE, WITH EMPHASIS ON SELECTED LOS ANGELES AND NEW YORK CITY MANAGEMENT EXPERIENCES

George H. Hagevik

PRAEGER PUBLISHERS
New York • Washington • London

The purpose of Praeger Special Studies is to make specialized research in U.S. and international economics and politics available to the academic, business, and government communities. For further information, write to the Special Projects Division, Praeger Publishers, Inc., 111 Fourth Avenue, New York, N.Y. 10003.

PRAEGER PUBLISHERS
111 Fourth Avenue, New York, N.Y. 10003, U.S.A.
5, Cromwell Place, London S.W.7, England

Published in the United States of America in 1970
by Praeger Publishers, Inc.

Second printing, 1971

Library of Congress Catalog Card Number: 72-112981

Printed in the United States of America

PREFACE

Air pollution is now recognized as one of the most serious environmental problems facing the United States today. The Air Quality Act of 1967 is the latest legislative response of the Federal Government to this problem, signaling the start of the present broad-scale regional attack on air pollution through the state governments. This attack will inevitably face many problems, particularly regarding issues that have economic, political, and institutional dimensions. This study, relying on experience in air pollution control in Los Angeles and New York City, attempts to point out ways of dealing with many of these problems.

In this volume, the air pollution problem today is defined in terms of the pollutants responsible, the technical aspects of control, the economic issues involved, and the political and institutional framework for dealing with the problem. The legal aspects of air pollution control are reviewed, along with the potential role of effluent fees, payments, and direct regulation in pollution abatement. It is found that each of these three approaches to abatement has shortcomings along with advantages. Direct regulation, due to its popularity with administrators and the fact that it allows for regulation under uncertainty, is shown to be an approach that will be widely used even though its adoption will mean higher costs in the long run.

Decision strategies that have some utility in air quality management are noted, with the role of bargaining given major emphasis. Investigations of bargaining behavior are reviewed, and conclusions are derived that are applicable to air quality management. The point is made that while bargaining is often viewed as a constraint in the rational decision model, it can also be used to promote efficiency.

The case studies of Los Angeles and New York City point up useful strategies for air quality management programs and note pitfalls that should be avoided. The case studies and review of the literature provide the basis for a decision model in air quality management that gives major emphasis to dealing with uncertainty. A number of techniques broadly defined as "bargaining behavior" form the framework for resolving major issues and promoting progress toward a least-cost solution to pollution abatement. The objective of such a management program is to avoid the costs of litigation wherever possible and provide a basis for effective management in the dim light of partial knowledge.

ACKNOWLEDGMENTS

The preparation of a volume such as this tries the patience of not only the writer but also those with which he closely associates. My wife, performing numerous roles, has performed admirably. Dr. Maynard Hufschmidt, Professor of City and Regional Planning and Environmental Engineering at the University of North Carolina, Chapel Hill, first interested me in this topic and continually separated the pertinent from the trivial in all stages of the work. Near the end, his assistance in pulling the disparate ends together was invaluable. A. C. Stern, Professor of Air Hygiene, School of Public Health, University of North Carolina, Chapel Hill, used his considerable expertise in the air pollution field to correct a number of technical points and to add a useful perspective to the two case studies.

Robert Barsky, Assistant Director of the Los Angeles Air Pollution Control District, cheerfully sat through hours of interviewing. David Mix, Assistant Los Angeles County Counsel, was also the source of much useful information. Len Tower of the Air Pollution Control District helped me find my way through 20 years' accumulation of department files. Arthur Atkisson of the Institute of Urban Ecology at the University of Southern California was of early assistance in pointing out key issues in the effort to control air pollution in Los Angeles.

James Harwood, Attorney for the Federal Power Commission, provided numerous briefs from cases dealing with air pollution in both Los Angeles and New York City. Carolyn Konheim, Public Information Officer for the New York City Department of Air Resources, and formerly president of Citizens for Clean Air, arranged a number of interviews and spent

hours herself being interviewed. Stanley Penil and
Murray Herman of Mayor John Lindsay's Office of Administration provided a useful perspective on air
pollution control efforts in New York City and also
supplied a number of hard-to-obtain reports and
memoranda.

Acknowledgment must also be given to the environmental health fellowship program of the U.S.
Public Health Service for financial support during
the course of this study.

CONTENTS

LIST OF TABLES AND FIGURES

PART **I**

LOOKING AT AIR POLLUTION CONTROL:
THE PAST AND MODELS FOR CHANGE

CHAPTER **1** THE STATUS OF
AIR QUALITY
MANAGEMENT

Air pollution is typical of many environmental
problems in that it has been with us for some time
but has only recently grown to a scale where differences in degree begin to become differences in
kind. Up to some level of concentration, disposal
of wastes is for the most part a local irritation.
But, at a certain threshold, costs to society start
to increase significantly. This phenomenon has resulted in a considerable redefinition of problems.
For example, in the case of air pollution, the concern is no longer as much with smoke damage as with
harm from photochemical smog.

The sources of air pollution today are complex
and varied. At the risk of oversimplification, it
can be said that there are four categories of activities responsible for air pollution: manufacturing, combustion of fuels, incineration, and
transportation. The Public Health Service estimates
that about 60 per cent of the particulates and gases
released into the air in the United States comes
from the transportation category, primarily from
automobiles. Air polluting substances are also
often divided into two categories. The first consists of stable primary pollutants that are not
changed in the air and consequently are traced with
comparative ease to their source. These are in the
form of dust, smoke, gas fumes, and droplets. Secondary pollutants are those produced by photochemical or physiochemical interactions between primary
pollutants in the air; they are difficult to trace
to a specific source because they do not originate
directly from any industrial, municipal, or residential source.

The most common physical and chemical classification of air pollutants includes six items: carbon

3

monoxide, sulfur oxides, nitrogen oxides, hydrocarbons, particulates, and the more amorphous photochemical smog.[1] Carbon monoxide, frequently found in heavy traffic, can produce headaches, loss of visual acuity, and decreased muscular coordination. Sulfur oxides, found where coal and oil are burned, corrode stone and metal and at higher concentrations reduce visibility, injure vegetation, and contribute in some measure to respiratory diseases. In addition to contributing to photochemical smog, nitrogen oxides, formed by the combustion of fuels, are thought to contribute along with particulate matter to the light brown haze that impairs scenic views. Hydrocarbons, discharged chiefly by the automobile, play a major role in the formation of photochemical smog, a complex mixture of gases and particulates manufactured by sunlight out of raw materials--nitrogen oxides and hydrocarbons--and discharged into the air mainly by automobiles. It can damage crops and trees, deteriorate rubber and other materials, reduce visibility, cause the eyes to smart and the throat to sting, and is thought to reduce resistance to respiratory diseases. Particulate matter, in addition to being a soiling agent, acts as a catalyst in the formation of other pollutants, contributes to the corrosion of metals, and in certain particle sizes can carry into the lungs irritant gases which might otherwise remain in the upper respiratory tract.

The mix of pollutants in the air varies from city to city depending upon the sources of pollutants, weather conditions, and local topography. At one extreme is Los Angeles, where a large percentage of the air pollution is photochemical smog caused by automobile emissions. Somewhere near the opposite end of the continuum is New York City, where sulfur dioxide and particulate matter are major air pollutants and the contribution of automobile emissions to ambient air pollution levels is judged to be, in a relative sense, less significant. Air pollution abatement programs thus require differing emphasis depending upon the pollutants identified within a given area.

These complicated mixtures of air pollutants are bothersome today not only because of the increasing production of pollutants but also because of higher expectations on the part of the population of metropolitan areas which has resulted in reduced

tolerance for air pollution that impairs the quality
of the environment. Thus, increasing public pressure
on officials at all levels of government to intensify air pollution abatement programs is becoming
an almost universal occurrence.

CONTROL AT THE LOCAL LEVEL

The current magnitude and changing nature of
the problem suggest a new or at least broader view
of planning for air quality management than has been
taken in the past. This is necessary because the
regulatory machinery for dealing with the air pollution problem has been and still is of a primitive
variety. Attempts to control air pollution in the
United States have been based on the traditional
delegation of police, public health, and nuisance
powers to local governments. Although larger cities
have had air pollution control ordinances since the
late 1940's or earlier, it is a valid generalization
that a majority of cities and towns in the United
States have until the last decade operated under
a general nuisance ordinance. Under this approach,
smoke is considered a nuisance in common law but
not a nuisance in and of itself. In each case,
proof was required that the smoke or emission was in
fact injurious or offensive to the senses. The law
of nuisance requires a showing of injury and, further, that some person as the source of such injury
is liable. It is often difficult, if not impossible,
to prove in a court of law that air pollution is in
fact injurious either to health or to property.
Furthermore, in a densely developed urban area with
a multitude of sources, one emitter can seldom be
said to be the cause and consequently liable in the
contest of a nuisance suit.

To avoid these problems, current statutes enacted on the local level declare the emission of
black smoke of a specified density to be a nuisance
per se, thereby doing away with the requirement of
proving on a case-by-case basis that such smoke
causes injury.[2] Such enactments have been held to
be a proper exercise of the police power. Recent
statutes have also avoided the difficulties of the
common law doctrine of nuisance and have simply declared that the emission of a contaminant into the
air is a public offense. The validity of these

statutes or ordinances does not depend on whether
the act of emission is a nuisance but whether they
come within constitutional considerations of certainty, reasonableness, and reasonable classification, as is the case for any statute or ordinance.
Thus, most air pollution legislation at the local
level has been directed toward limitations on the
density and opacity of smoke. Even where the control law is more extensive, most enforcement efforts
have been directed against smoke because it is easily
visible and can therefore be obviously labeled as
a source of ambient air pollution. The typical
urban smoke control law, such as Los Angeles Air
Pollution Control District rule 50, simply limits
the density, opacity, and length of time of smoke
emission.

> A person shall not discharge into
> the atmosphere from any single
> source of emission whatsoever any
> air contaminants for a period or
> periods aggregating more than three
> minutes in any one hour which is:
> (a) As dark or darker in shade as
> that designated as #2 on the Ringel-
> mann Chart, as published by the
> United States Bureau of Mines, or
> (b) Of such opacity as to obscure
> an observer's view to a degree
> equal to or greater than does smoke
> described in subsection (a) of the
> Rule.

The Ringelmann chart, a series of different colored
squares which can be compared to smoke coming from
stacks, provides a scale for comparing the darkness
and opaqueness of visible smoke to absolute levels.

Most of the legislation is basically similar
to zoning legislation.[3] For example, most air pollution laws either establish fixed emission standards
or delegate the setting of the contemplated standards
to an air pollution control agency. Another common
provision is to require the installation of specific
control devices to abate pollutant emissions. But,
because the imposition of fixed standards and the
requirement of specific control devices may prove
in many cases to be very costly and may raise potential constitutional problems, the statutes generally

provide for variances to be granted by an air pollution control agency. A typical variance provision
is found in an Illinois statute:

> The Board may grant individual var-
> iances beyond the limitations pre-
> scribed in this Act, whenever it is
> found, upon presentation of adequate
> proof that compliance with any pro-
> vision of this Act, or any rule or
> regulation, requirement or order of
> the Board, will result in an arbi-
> trary and unreasonable taking of
> property or in the practical clos-
> ing and elimination of any unlawful
> business, occupation or activity,
> in either case without sufficient
> corresponding benefit or advantage
> to the people.[4]

The hardship required to be shown is a considerable
one, though much is left to agency and court interpretation. One could conclude that, although the
typical statutory language appears to permit variances only in extreme cases--perhaps only in those
having constitutional dimensions*--an agency

---

*The reference to the constitutional problem
simply refers to the general principle that the
state cannot curtail one's use of his property without paying "just compensation." The concept of
"taking," which appears in the statute, is a constitutional concept which defines whether or not
compensation must be paid, and it is applied rather
inconsistently. Still, it is possible that curtail-
ment of the property owner's rights to pollute may
be classified as a "taking" unless a strong case
can be made based on regulation for public health
and use of the police power. When aesthetic and
generalized environmental quality goals are emphasized, constitutional doubts are increased. See
L. Pollack, "Legal Boundaries of Air Pollution Con-
trol--State and Local Legislative Purpose and Techniques," Journal of Law and Contemporary Problems,
XXX (Spring, 1968), 331-54; F. Michelman, "Property,
Utility, and Fairness: Comments on the Ethical
Foundations of Just Compensation Law," Harvard Law
Review, LXXX (March, 1967), 1165.

might, by seizing on the requirement that there be a "corresponding benefit or advantage," attempt an extensive comparison of benefits and costs. On balance, however, existing local legislation in the United States appears to give little sanction to methods of decision-making that utilize a step-by-step comparison of benefits and costs. This is the case even though it has been estimated that air pollution abatement during the rest of this century will cost vast sums of money, possibly billions of dollars.[5]

THE POLITICAL AND INSTITUTIONAL FRAMEWORK

As noted, until recently, attempts at air quality management in this country have been viewed almost entirely as a local responsibility. Still, the role of the states in air quality management needs to be treated because of the states' "residual sovereignty" which allows them to invest local governments and special districts with authority to act. The states and their court systems stand in a key position, not only by virtue of the federal system, but also because of the common law which by tradition has invested them with authority. The common law and the U.S. Constitution, which delegates major powers to the states, together make the states in theory the bodies most capable of carrying to the local level the burdens of regulation and enforcement.[6]

California and New York State are important examples of experience to date of the few states that have been actively involved in air pollution control.[7] The 1947 California legislation was the first broad state air pollution control program in that it authorized any California county to activate an Air Pollution Control District by resolution of the County Board of Supervisors declaring the need for the District to function.[8] The District was granted the power to "make and enforce all needful orders, rules, and regulation,"[9] and was given wide discretion in attacking individual local conditions. The only state-wide prohibition was the restriction of smoke emission to level #2 on the Ringelmann scale for a maximum of three minutes in any hour.[10]

The intent of the California legislation is well spelled out in Section 24242 of the California

Health and Safety Code, which the Los Angeles Air
Pollution Control District has considered as the
critical section of its enabling legislation.   The
section states:

> A person shall not discharge from
> any source whatsoever such quan-
> tities of air contaminants or other
> material which cause injury, detri-
> ment, nuisance or annoyance to any
> considerable number of persons or
> to the comfort, repose, health or
> safety of any such persons or the
> public or which cause or have a
> natural tendency to cause injury
> or damage to business or property.

The California Air Pollution Control District
Act also provided that local ordinances could
still be used to fight air pollution despite the
creation of county-wide districts with rule-making
power.[11]   In practice, however, the districts
have been more active than local governments in
attacking the problem.   The state has also provided
guidelines for these districts by classifying
pollutant concentrations in levels according to
the qualities "adverse," "serious," and "emergency,"
based upon measurable effects.

New York State, in contrast, has established
objectives that vary according to a regional
classification, based on land use, of industrial,
commercial, residential, and rural.[12]   Different
air quality standards, generally related to the
possibility of practical accomplishment, are
established for each regional classification.   Thus,
rural areas are required to have the cleanest air
and industrial areas are permitted to have dirtier
air.

New York State has gone a step further in that
the state control agency may adopt rules prescribing
minimum standards for the state as a whole.[13]   But,
as in many state air pollution laws, a nonpre-
emption clause is included in the legislation.   In
New York, all local laws, rules, and regulations
not inconsistent with state-wide enactments and
complying with the minimum state standards may be
enforced by the locality.[14]

Recent Federal Responses to Air Pollution

The increasing concern with air pollution over time can best be illustrated by looking at the federal responses to the problem. In the last decade and a half, the Federal Government has devoted increasing attention to air pollution as the public at large and governmental officials and legislators have perceived that it is becoming an increasingly serious problem. Congress first voted to give the Federal Government a role in air quality management in 1955. In that year, the Federal Air Pollution Control Act of 1955 was adopted,[15] authorizing the Public Health Service to conduct a program of research, technical assistance to state and local governments, training of technical personnel, and dissemination of information. The Federal Government's role was limited to determining the nature of the problem, with the law specifically reserving to the states and local governments the primary responsibility for air quality management. This act resulted in the emergence of a Public Health Service philosophy that the agency should not have primary responsibility for the control of air pollution, but rather that its role should be a supporting one of research and technical assistance.

During this early period, the basic objectives of the Public Health Service's program were threefold: (1) to improve the status of knowledge of the causes and effects of air pollution and the means of controlling it within acceptable limits; (2) to apply present and future knowledge to the actual control of air pollutants through technical assistance to states, communities, and industry; and (3) to stimulate government at all levels, industry, and the general public to give increased attention and greater resources to the prevention and control of air pollution.[16]

Slow but steady progress was made in control and abatement of pollution under this act. But, probably more significant, it drew the attention of the scientific community--physicians, engineers, chemists, meteorologists, and biologists particularly--to the technical problems associated with air pollution control. The research and technical assistance program helped to bring into focus the concern of medical science that air pollution probably contributes to many of the more serious diseases

of the respiratory system--asthma, bronchitis, and
lung cancer. Research accomplished under provisions
of the act demonstrated that air pollution, which
previously had been regarded largely as a nuisance,
was also a threat to both health and property on
a broad front.[17]

By 1958, both inside and outside of government,
concern with air pollution had risen to the point
that the Public Health Service sponsored a national
conference in which sentiment was tested for possible next steps in attacking the problem. Much
attention was given during the conference to the
need for further development of medical and biological evidence to support the public health
argument for air quality management in general.[18]
During this period, a systematic collection of
evidence on photochemical smog outside of California
was just beginning, and a half dozen bills were being introduced by California congressmen to extend
the financing of the 1955 act.[19] In 1960, the
Surgeon General of the Public Health Service established the Division of Air Pollution, which gave
significant organizational status to the program.
By 1962, feeling had built up in Congress to significantly extend the federal role in the air pollution control field, particularly as to interstate
abatement proceedings. This feeling, together
with an increasing general concern outside of
government for air pollution, provided the stimulus
for the Department of Health, Education and Welfare
sponsored second National Air Pollution Conference
in late 1962.[20] Significant during this conference
was a shift in approach on the health issue from the
specificity of cause and effect to emphasis upon
multiple-agent causation. Thus, chronic respiratory
problems in humans were acknowledged to develop over
a number of years, exacerbated if not caused by
many possible chemicals in the atmosphere in addition to bacterial infection and cigarette smoking.
As G. Siegel has pointed out, this concept of
multiple-agent effect in disease, which is broadly
accepted in the field of preventive medicine, was
given considerable emphasis in conference conclusions.[21] Most presentations of evidence of health
hazards at congressional hearings prior to this
time were attempts to relate specific effects to
individual causes.[22]

On February 7, 1963, President Kennedy sent
a special message to Congress entitled "Improving

America's Health," in which he called for new legislation to strengthen and intensify federal air
pollution control efforts in four broad areas: more
intensive research, federal grants for starting
and improving control programs by state and local
governments, studies on nation-wide air pollution
problems, and federal action to abate interstate
air pollution.[23] By this time, there existed
broad scientific and public recognition that control
action to meet the subtle as well as the gross
challenges of air pollution was lagging behind the
need.[24] Lacking, however, was a generally accepted
body of scientific knowledge on photochemical smog
and on the exact nature of air pollution problems
in specific areas. This lack of data was noted
in a report prepared for the Senate Special Subcommittee on Air and Water Pollution: "Because of
the expense of necessary equipment and lack of
trained personnel very few localities have obtained
comprehensive data on their air quality."[25]

The lack of an energetic response by states
and cities in controlling air pollution under the
legislation of the previous decade had also clearly
demonstrated the need for additional federal effort,
and Congress took remedial action by passing the
Clean Air Act of 1963.[26] Its passage started the
trend toward the development of a national policy
on air quality management. The act included for
the first time a limited federal regulatory authority for abating specific air pollution problems.
This authority was intended to supplement the
abatement powers of state and local governments
in two types of situations. First, for an interstate problem in which pollution arising in one
state could endanger the health or welfare of per-
sons in another state, the Secretary of Health,
Education and Welfare could on his own initiative
or on official request as specified in the act,
initiate formal proceedings for the necessary abatement. (The only way a continuing interstate program
could be brought into being was through the development of an interstate compact and its ratification,
both by the legislatures of the states involved and
by Congress.) Second, for an air pollution problem
that is purely intrastate in nature, the Secretary
could invoke formal abatement proceedings only on
official request from designated officials in the
state involved.

The provisions for regulatory abatement procedures included conferences with the cognizant official agencies, public hearings, and, finally, court action. The abatement activity could be terminated, of course, at the initial or second step of the process if the problem was resolved. The 1963 act also directed the Department of Health, Education and Welfare (HEW) to develop and promulgate criteria of air quality for the guidance of state and local authorities in establishing ambient air quality standards. Use of these criteria was not to be mandatory; rather they were to be used as guides for state and local agencies.

In October, 1964, the Senate Special Subcommittee on Air and Water Pollution submitted the report "Steps Toward Cleaner Air,"[27] in which legislation was recommended to regulate emissions from gasoline-powered motor vehicles. In January, 1965, Senator Edmund Muskie introduced legislation to achieve this end, and the bill was subsequently passed.[28] This development is noted since previous laws precisely proscribed federal replacement of state and local responsibility. With automobile emission control legislation, the Federal Government moved into standard-setting and enforcement in a significant way.

The 1966 National Air Pollution Conference, in keeping with a rising nation-wide concern with environmental quality problems in general, attracted national attention and a significantly larger attendance than previous conferences.[29] Thus, by early 1967, the President and the Congress were both reflecting and stimulating an increased public concern about air pollution. The President proposed sweeping new authority for HEW, including the establishment of national emission standards, whereby certain industries would be subject to uniform nation-wide controls regardless of plant location and atmospheric conditions.[30] The view prevailed in Congress, however, that solutions to air pollution problems required flexibility and different approaches for different regions, so the Air Quality Act of 1967 in final form did not require these national standards for specific industries.[31]

The act, which amended the Clean Air Act of 1964, has as one of its objectives the state control of air pollution problems, which is a reflection of

a belief that federal control would not be desirable
and that differences in controls in different regions taking into account varying atmospheric,
topographic, industrial, and other conditions are
at this time necessary.[32] Pollution abatement
activities are to be coordinated in air quality
regions designated by HEW and will be guided by air
quality criteria and recommended control techniques
developed by HEW for specific pollution agents,
and are to be in accord with air quality standards
and enforcement plans developed by the states. HEW
is authorized to establish standards if a state
fails to act or if state action is considered inadequate, and to enforce these standards by court
action to stop pollution in emergency situations
endangering health, regardless of the economic or
technological feasibility of pollution control.[33]

THE IMPACT OF PRESENT LEGISLATION

        The passage of the Air Quality Act of 1967 and
the number of prior congressional hearings on air
pollution documented the fact that by the mid-1960's
air pollution was no longer perceived as a local
problem. In the past, efforts at air quality control have been given low priority by most local
governments. With the significant exceptions of
Los Angeles, where a distinctive problem related
to photochemical smog resulted in the formation of
a very active air pollution control agency, and
some other cities such as Pittsburgh and St. Louis,
where smoke was a problem, federal activity has
been the first sign that air quality management
would be given some priority in many urban areas.
As noted above, the Air Quality Act assigns primary
responsibility for devising the regulatory mechanism
for controlling air pollution to state governments.
The act provides that states shall be provided with
federally determined air quality criteria and control techniques once they are promulgated by HEW,
which is also granted power to review the standards
established and the proposed plan of enforcement.[34]
Although the use of these criteria and techniques
is not mandatory, it is apparently contemplated by
Congress that new state and local legislation will
be forthcoming, and this expectation coupled with
an expression in the act that pollution control must
be undertaken selectively in light of technological

and economic feasibility,* suggests that new thought
should be given to devising machinery that will be
capable of doing this job most effectively.

A first concern is that existing approaches to
decision-making in air quality management on the
state and local level in the United States need to
be examined in some detail and compared to theoretical ideals. This is desirable since the increasing magnitude of the problem will most likely call
for changes in these traditional approaches.

THE SCOPE OF THE STUDY

The public's perception that air pollution
deteriorates the quality of the urban environment
is increasingly resulting in pressure on air pollution control officials to significantly intensify
their control efforts. Such a mandate calls for
serious consideration of alternative courses of
action. This study is an attempt at such a consideration. The focus is on a view of decision-
making in air quality management that emphasizes
economic theory and operationally valid approaches.

One hypothesis is that decision-making in air
quality management can be improved by utilizing not
only the technical knowledge of the engineer and
the skills of the economist, but also by relying on
behavioral research from other social sciences.
Various possible approaches to decision-making in
air quality management are examined, including the
economist's rational decision model (detailed in
Chapter 2), which deals with objectives, criteria,
constraints and benefit-cost analysis, the minimum-
cost solution (a special case of the rational model),
and various behavioral views. Emphasis is given to
the role of bargaining behavior in decision-making,
for air quality management is not a question of

---

*Section 107 (c) provides, "Such recommendations
shall include such data as are available on the
latest available technology and economic feasibility
of alternative methods of prevention and control
of air contamination including cost effectiveness
analyses."

absolutes--of clean air versus dirty air--but of
finding an accommodation between those who assert
that users of the air should keep it as clean as
technically possible and those who would delay
action until the nature of abatement costs and
control technology are better understood. Conclusions from research on bargaining are noted that
might be applied to conflict resolution situations
in air quality management.

A precondition for investigating decision-
making in air quality management is some understanding of the technical issues involved. These
technical considerations to a very considerable
degree determine the "rules of the game" and the
constraints within which decisions must be made.
Thus, Chapter 4 reviews three approaches to air
pollution control--direct control, use of effluent
fees and charges, and subsidies--which can be used
within our political and institutional system to
abate pollution.

The sections dealing with social science theory
and the technical issues set the stage for two case
studies of air quality management in New York City
and Los Angeles.* Although pollution control

----

*The case study approach is suggested by O.
Herfindahl and A. Kneese, Quality of the Environment
(Baltimore: The Johns Hopkins Press, 1965), p. 90.
Because the automobile is a special type of pollution emitter which is very mobile, it is not dealt
with directly in this study. But it can be said
that a national emission standard is currently in
effect which is so written that it becomes more
restrictive with the passage of time. The automobile industry response to this standard has been
to redesign engines to allow for more efficient
combustion of fuels. See U.S. Department of Health,
Welfare and Education, Automobile Air Pollution,
Second Report of the Secretary of Health, Education
and Welfare to the U.S. Congress (Washington, D.C.:
Government Printing Office, July 15, 1955) and
Progress in the Prevention and Control of Air
Pollution, First Report of the Secretary of Health,
Education and Welfare to the U.S. Congress (Washing-
ton, D.C.: Government Printing Office, June 28,
1968), pp. 15-28.

efforts in these two very large urban areas are
somewhat atypical (in the sense that the Los Angeles
case study deals with a pioneering effort at control
of a very serious smog problem, while the New York
City experience illustrates numerous pitfalls that
have been avoided in other cities), the complexities
of the institutional and political environments in
which air quality decisions have been made are well
represented.

The case study material provides the basis for
an attempt at integrating various views of decision-
making with the economist's rational model and the
minimum-cost solution. The hypothesis that total
costs can be minimized by allowing for bargaining
behavior in air quality decision-making is analyzed.
More specifically, it is anticipated that bargaining behavior, by bringing unforeseen costs into the
open, will be a very useful tool for dealing with
uncertainty and reducing the opposition of those
who are to be controlled. After this evaluation,
a hypothetical regulatory program for dealing with
stationary sources of air pollution is developed
based on the earlier conclusions. This hypothetical
program is only partially based on existing control
efforts and is conceived in the understanding that
regulatory officials must be enabled to operate
effectively even in the dim light of partial knowledge defining and relating the social and technological aspects of air pollution. Inasmuch as the
program is merely sketched, it will serve not as a
detailed blueprint but more as a stimulus to new
thinking about air quality management.

NOTES

1. For a more detailed but still brief state-
ment of air pollutants and their effects, see U.S.
Department of Health, Education and Welfare, Today
and Tomorrow in Air Pollution, Public Health Service
Publication 1555 (Washington, D.C.: Government
Printing Office, n.d.). A more extended review is
found in A. C. Stern (ed.), Air Pollution, Vol. I
(New York: Academic Press, 1968).

2. H. Kennedy, "Legal Aspects of Air Pollution
Control," Public Health Reports, LXXIX (August, 1964),
688.

3.   See L. Pollack, "Legal Boundaries of Air Pollution Control--State and Local Legislative Purpose and Techniques," Journal of Law and Contemporary Problems, XXX (Spring, 1968), 331-54.

4.   Illinois Revised Statues, Chapter III 1/2, Section 240.11.

5.   J. Hanks and H. Kuble, "Industry Action to Curb Pollution," Harvard Business Review, XLIV (September - October, 1966), 49-62.

6.   See T. Williams, "Experience with Clean Air Act" (Paper presented at the Third Conference on Air Pollution Control at Purdue University, October 27, 1964, for state experience in air pollution control).

7.   For other states, see U.S. Department of Health, Education and Welfare, A Digest of State Air Pollution Laws, Public Health Service Publication 711, (Washington, D.C.: Government Printing Office, 1966). Also see: J. Cohen, "Interstate Compacts--An Evaluation," Journal of the Air Pollution Control Association, XVII (October, 1967), 676-78; C. Yaffe, "A Roll Call of the States--Where Do We Stand in State and Interstate Air Pollution Control," Proceedings, National Conference on Air Pollution, U.S. Department of Health, Education and Welfare, Public Health Service Publication 1649, (Washington, D.C.: Government Printing Office, 1966), pp. 359-62.

8.   Air Pollution Control District Act, California Health and Safety Code, Section 24198-24323 (West, 1967).

9.   Ibid., Section 24260.

10.   See note 3.

11.   Air Pollution Control District Act, op. cit., Section 24247-48.

12.   "Rules for the Prevention and Control of Air Contamination and Air Pollution," New York State Department of Health, Board of Air Pollution Control, 1967.

13.   Ibid.

14. New York Public Health Law, Section 1297 (McKinney 1966).

15. Public Law 84-159.

16. U.S. Senate, A Study of Pollution--Air (Staff report to the Committee on Public Works), 88th Cong., 1st Sess., September, 1963, p. 29.

17. Williams, op. cit.

18. U.S. Department of Health, Education and Welfare, Proceedings, National Conference on Air Pollution, November 12-20, 1958, Public Health Service Publication 654 (Washington, D.C.: Government Printing Office, 1959). See particularly pp. 219, 228-53.

19. U.S. House of Representatives, Air Pollution Control, 86th Cong., 1st Sess., House Report 960, 1959, p. 75. See also U.S. House of Representatives, Air Pollution Control Progress Review, Hearings before the House Interstate and Foreign Commerce Committee, 86th Cong., 2nd Sess., February 23, 24, 1960.

20. U.S. Department of Health, Education and Welfare, Proceedings, National Conference on Air Pollution, December 10-12, 1962, Public Health Service Publication 1022 (Washington, D.C.: Government Printing Office, 1962).

21. G. Siegel, "The National Government Evolves into the Vehicle Emission Field" (unpublished manuscript, Air Pollution Control Institute, University of Southern California, June, 1967), p. 28. See 1962 Proceedings, op. cit., p. 389.

22. For the earlier view, see U.S. House of Representatives, Unburned Hydrocarbons, 58th Cong., 2nd Sess., House Report 231, 1958.

23. U.S. House of Representatives, Air Pollution, 88th Cong., 1st Sess., House Report 508, 1963, p. 15.

24. Williams, op. cit.

25. U.S. Senate, Air Pollution Control, 88th Cong., 1st Sess., Senate Report 638, 1963, p. 441.

26.   Public Law 88-206.

27.   Congressional Record, January 7, 1965, Vol. III, No. 4, p. 283.

28.   Public Law 89-272.

29.   1966 Proceedings, op. cit.   This conference was only part of an increasing concern for environmental quality that was evident in Washington.   See U.S. House of Representatives, The Adequacy of Technology for Pollution Abatement (A report of the Research Management Advisory Panel through the Subcommittee on Science, Research, and Development to the Committee on Science and Astronautics), 89th Cong., 2nd Sess., July 1, 1966; U.S. House of Representatives, Environmental Pollution: A Challenge co Science and Technology (A report of the Subcommittee on Science, Research, and Development to the Committee on Science and Astronautics), 89th Cong., 2nd Sess., October 1, 1966.   For later statements, see U.S. House of Representatives, Managing the Environment (A report of the Subcommittee on Science and Astronautics), 90th Cong., 2nd Sess., June 17, 1968; U.S. Senate, Congressional White Paper on a National Policy for the Environment (Submitted to Congress under the auspices of the Committee on Interior and Insular Affairs, U.S. Senate, and the Committee on Science and Astronautics, U.S. House of Representatives, 90th Cong., 2nd Sess., October, 1968.

30.   See U.S. Senate, Air Pollution--1966, Hearings before a Subcommittee on Air and Water Pollution of the Committee on Public Works, 89th Cong., 2nd Sess., Senate Report 780, June 7, 8, 14, 15, 1966; U.S. Senate, Air Pollution--1967, Hearings before the Subcommittee on Air and Water Pollution of the Committee on Public Works, 90th Cong., 1st Sess., February 13-May 18, 1967.   The latter totals 2,693 pages in four volumes.

31.   Public Law 90-148.

32.   Ibid., Section 108 (a).

33.   For an analysis of the act, see R. Martin and L. Symington, "A Guide to the Air Quality Act of 1967," Journal of Law and Contemporary Problems, XXX (Winter, 1968), 239-74.

34.   Ibid., Section 107 (c).

CHAPTER **2** WELFARE ECONOMICS
AND AIR QUALITY
MANAGEMENT

Readings in welfare economics published during
the last thirty years are replete with references
to smoke damage as a classic instance of what are
called negative externalities.[1] Although seemingly
providing a sound theoretical foundation for analyzing problems of externalities such as those
associated with air pollution, welfare economics has
found very little application in this area. Why
is this the case? Although it is commonly argued
that the limiting conditions introduced as a part
of economic theory have restricted its usefulness
for dealing with practical problems such as air quality management, it is also true that prior to 1950
there was little interest on the part of economists
in externalities. One of the few available references on the economist's approach to air quality
management prior to the 1960's was a chapter from
William Kapp's The Social Cost of Private Enterprise, which was published in 1950.[2] Only in this
decade have the social scientists "discovered" the
air pollution problem and joined a field that formerly attracted primarily engineers and physical
scientists. The best indicator to date of the economist's increased interest is probably the 1966
publication of The Economics of Air Pollution, ed-
ited by Harold Wolozin.[3]

The practitioner looking for immediately useful
answers in this volume will be disappointed, for it
is little more than a summary--albeit an excellent
one--of the state of the art. The primary contribution of the book is that it brings relevant economic
theory to bear on the problem, explicitly or implicitly reveals the advantages and weaknesses of the
economist's approach, and suggests data deficiencies
and research needs. The consensus of the participants in the forum from which the book was drawn is

that the economics problem has been defined and that
the task for the next few years is to gather data
and do research that might lead to estimates of the
necessary answers. If an analogy to water quality
management holds, the estimate of a few years is
optimistic.[4]

Still, inasmuch as since air pollution is in a
fundamental sense a social and economic problem that
must be handled within a complex political and institutional framework, the economist's rational
model is relevant. It is particularly valuable because, although technological means are currently
available to purify the air to any desired degree,
costs increase significantly as higher degrees of
air quality are sought. (The technological problem
that remains to be solved is the development of a
method of monitoring levels of emission accurately
and at low cost.) The economist's view of air quality management is important because we are finally
perceiving a condition of scarcity so central to his
thinking. Air is now viewed as a congested facility.
Without the attempt at evaluation he provides, the
desirable objective of an air quality management
program of reducing the level of pollution in the
atmosphere by the least costly means possible would
be difficult to achieve. Since pollution abatement
is primarily a matter of avoiding costs, programs
need to be initially evaluated from an economic point
of view, for, as R. Turvey has noted, "even though
an economic calculation of gains or losses is often
not sufficient to reach a well based decision, it
is nearly always an essential preliminary."[5]

MAKING A RATIONAL CHOICE

Basic to the application of the welfare economics model to public management and investment decisions is the assumption of rationality and rational
behavior. Economics, operations research, and planning have evolved approaches to, or models of, rational decision-making that differ in detail and
emphasis but are alike in essential structure. This
approach commonly consists of four steps:

(1) Establishing goals or objectives whose
values are to be maximized subject to constraints which must be met;

(2) Developing operational standards and criteria from the objectives;

(3) Formulating an optimal plan, design, or course of action, using the standards and criteria;

(4) Evaluating the consequences of the plan, design or course of action in order to redefine the objectives if required.[6]

The essential aspect of the model is the maximization of the value of a multidimensional objective function subject to constraints imposed by technology and nature and, in the air quality management context, by political and institutional factors.[7] It is significant that meaningful objectives and criteria, reflecting social values, are formulated by politically responsible decision-makers in the legislative process, whereas detailed plans and programs on pollution abatement are formulated administratively. Requirements of the model include extensive debate and awareness on the part of the participants of information on the expected consequences of courses of action.

Objectives and Constraints

The objective function is a rule which allows one to compute the benefits and costs associated with diverse objectives in a common metric. One approach is to express all benefits and costs in terms of money, so that maximizing the value of the objective function would correspond to maximizing the net value of a proposed air quality management program in actual or imputed market value terms that can be related directly to economic welfare.* This

---

*Most economists would apply the money measure to the objective of economic efficiency only, and handle other objectives such as income distribution qualitatively or as constraints. Arthur Maass holds that at least the distribution objective can be combined with economic efficiency in a single weighted objective function. See A. Maass, "Benefit-Cost Analysis--Its Relevance for Public Investment Decisions," Quarterly Journal of Economics, LXXX (May, 1966), 208-26; R. Havemann, "Comment," Quarterly Journal of Economics, LXXXI (November, 1967), 695-702.

is essentially a benefit-cost view since one may
alternatively refer to damages (costs) avoided as
benefits and the costs incurred for air pollution
abatement as costs and say that pollution reduction
up to but not beyond a certain point will maximize
benefits minus costs.

The maximization may be constrained by all the
real world limitations--physical, social, political,
and biological. In practical terms, these constraints could be technological (representing the
techniques by which real resources may be combined
to produce the program outputs and, hence, benefits),
resource based (reflecting the upper limits on real
resources available for application on a program),
or political (such as an upper or lower limit on the
feasible degree of control of private industry).

The interchangeability of objectives and constraints is an important aspect of this decision
model. In solving a constrained maximum problem,
one can obtain an indication of the marginal cost of
honoring a particular constraint by developing a
plan that honors the constraint and an alternative
plan that relaxes the constraint, and computing the
difference in the value of the objective function in
the two plans.[8]

The three fundamental relationships involved in
the solution of the maximization problem are the
relation of resource cost to input, the relation of
benefit to output, and the relation of output to in-
put--formally specified as the cost-input function,
the benefit-output function, and the production
function.[9] In the decision model, the planning
process consists of the identification of the param-
eters and the values of these functions in the formulation of a plan that maximizes the value of the
objective function subject to all applicable constraints.

Objectives

Although there are considerable differences in
the nature of air pollution problems in different
parts of the United States, any classification of
damage costs from such pollution inevitably has social, biological, and psychological characteristics.
Of critical concern, then, is a determination of the

objectives of air quality management. Is the objective the protection of human health, the prevention
of economic losses, the preservation of aesthetic
and scenic values of the environment, or some sub-
set of all these objectives? As noted, in the rational decision model the objectives are set up by
politically responsible decision-makers. If a social choice is made that necessitates more concern
than with just economic losses, the air pollution
control administrator immediately becomes concerned
with values that are difficult to measure in money
terms. These qualitative values can be dealt with
in two ways. One alternative is to label them as
intangibles and temporarily ignore them as objectives in planning an air quality management program.
When the proposed program is presented to the decision-makers, side information would be presented on
public health, aesthetics, and other considerations
relevant to making a decision in the public interest.

Constraints

Another more rigorous way of handling objectives that cannot be quantified in money terms is to
treat them as explicit requirements in any proposed
air quality management program. Hypotheses about
these intangible values could be included in the
planning process by stating them in physical terms
and treating them as constraints under the cost
minimization or net benefit maximization approach.[10]
Thus, if an objective is set that the air should be
clean enough not to affect visibility in the aesthetic sense or that some well-defined health hazard
is to be avoided, the management program would be
designed to achieve this at minimum cost.[11] This
may require a different management program than one
operating without the constraint. Assuming the constraints are effective (i.e., not automatically met
if quantifiable costs are minimized), they would result in a higher cost system than could otherwise
be achieved. The extra cost represents the limitation the constraint places upon achieving the least
quantifiable cost solution.

To be consistent with attempts at achieving a
minimum cost solution, the planning process should
consider constraints temporary and view them as considerations for further analysis to see how well
they represent social preferences. One approach to

this analysis, as noted above, is to test their cost
sensitivity. By varying a constraint by small
amounts, redetermining the optimal system, and relating the change in costs to the associated physical
changes, information can be provided to legislative
decision-makers that would, theoretically at least,
improve the quality of their decisions.[12]

Criteria and Standards

Criteria and standards in the general rational
model provide the detailed information that planners
require to formulate optimal plans. In general,
they include such guides as a discount rate, which
serves to place all cost and benefit streams on a
common basis in time; instructions on how to handle
uncertainty; weighting factors to be applied to capital and/or operation, maintenance, and replacement
costs; and a definition of the geographical area and
functional scope of the problem.[13] The objective
function is also an important design criterion in
that it defines the combination of objectives, their
relative weights, and their form.

These criteria can be used when applying the
rational decision model to air pollution and should
be viewed as tests or measures of effectiveness. As
such, they are evaluative devices. A clarification
is in order, however, since the Department of
Health, Education and Welfare additionally refers to
criteria as "guides" for the development of ambient
air quality standards.[14] Under this view, criteria
are production function relationships between ambient air pollution levels and the damages caused
by these levels. Accordingly, criteria are developed using the "state of the art" technological and
scientific judgments about the damages that result
from pollutants in various concentrations and during
various exposure times. As such, they are always
open to change in the light of new knowledge. They
provide the basis for deciding what is satisfactory
air quality, which pollutants must be controlled,
and the degree of control required. Depending on the
objectives and constraints specified, the effects
that might be considered are those which damage materials and vegetation, obscure light, interfere
with the normal functions of biological systems of
man and animals, impair health, and otherwise prevent enjoyment of life and property. In their

development, consideration is given to the dual factors of pollution concentrations and exposure times
as these in combination cause specific effects on
man, animals, vegetation, and other aspects of the
environment.[15]

A set of criteria commonly used are of a technical, engineering, or biological nature relating
to standards of public health and safety. These
air quality criteria form the basis for a pragmatic
variant of the formal model typically called the
"standards approach." For example, in terms of the
model, a traditional public health approach of establishing and enforcing a health standard can be
stated as achieving the least-cost means of meeting
a fixed requirement.* This differential between
the two views of criteria should be kept in mind.

In the air pollution control field, an air
quality standard is commonly defined as the maximum
quantity of an air pollutant a governmental agency
intends to allow in the ambient air within its jurisdiction. Unlike the air quality criteria that
specify relationships, the standard is thought of
as a specification of a legally enforceable state
for which the governmental agency will require compliance, using its authority.[16] In essence, it is
the level of air quality desired within a given
jurisdiction. This level can be achieved through
the use of emission or effluent standards that restrict the emission of pollutants from any given
source. Generally, they are stated in terms of measurable properties such as its quantity per unit of

---

*This approach has many advantages. By working
toward a fixed goal expressed in physical terms,
difficult problems of measuring values are avoided.
The problem is narrowly defined so that the possibility of finding a nearly optimal solution is increased. But limitations include the tentative and
expedient nature of standards which are often dis-
regarded by practitioners. H. Thomas points out
that the assignment of such standards implies a
value that can be measured in dollars--a marginal
benefit-cost ratio based on whatever data are available for judgment--but this is seldom done. H.
Thomas, "The Animal Farm: A Mathematical Model for
the Discussion of the Environment," Quarterly Journal of Economics, LXXVII (February, 1963), 143-48.

time, its concentration, color, opacity, height of
emission, or some other suitable means of measurement. Ideally, the standards imposed would vary
with different geographic locations. Such variations would be necessary to take into account the
differing waste assimilation capacity of the air-
shed of the governmental jurisdiction under varying
atmospheric conditions and the differing capacity
of various locations within the air-shed to diffuse
pollutants.

RATIONALITY AND THE MINIMUM-COST SOLUTION

This brief review of the rational decision
model points up the fact that the determination of
sound economic policy in air quality management requires an accurate and continuing evaluation of the
costs of abatement relative to air pollution damages. Viewing costs avoided as benefits, decisions
need to be sought that maximize the present value
of net benefits. Ideally, this analysis would be
directed toward finding abatement efforts that
equate incremental abatement costs and the value of
incremental damage costs reduced.* This quest for
what is commonly called "the minimum-cost solution"
is an elusive one. But within the more general
framework outlined above, with its emphasis on constraints, the theoretical ideal can more closely be
approached in an optimal manner.

It is useful to keep in mind the fact that
rational decision-making does not necessarily have

----

*Costs would be partially related to the con-
siderations of engineering feasibility, economic
acceptability to those controlled, and uncertainty.
It is significant, as P. Gerhardt points out, that
there has been far more interest in assessing the
value of the damages done by air pollution than in
the costs of control. The costs of recent levels
of control have been generally accepted as a frac-
tion of the total damages. The interest in incremental costs of control will increase as incremental
abatement costs rise and incremental damage costs
fall. P. Gerhardt, "Some Economic Aspects of Air
Pollution" (Paper presented at the Mid-Atlantic
States Section, Air Pollution Control Association
Conference, October 4, 1967), p. 2.

to rely on sophisticated tools for analysis. Even
an unsophisticated approach could measure abatement
costs so that they include both administrative costs
of control and capital and process change costs associated with abatement. (Recent research suggests
that narrowly circumscribed approaches to pollution
control are less effective than more flexible ones
in achieving large cost savings.)[17] Tools of evaluation, whether in sophisticated or crude form, need
to be applied not only to proposed theoretically
ideal schemes of effluent fees and charges, but also
to commonly used approaches such as emission standards under programs of direct regulation.

But this analytical view of objectives, constraints, criteria, and standards only provides us
with the tools for evaluating the economic aspects
of air quality management decisions. It is, therefore, a necessary but not sufficient instrument for
fully understanding how decisions are made and determining how they might be improved. It must also
in some manner be related to the political and social behavior of the individuals and organizations
involved in the making of decisions on air quality.

NOTES

1. The original source is A. Pigou, The Economics of Welfare (London: Macmillan & Co., 1932),
pp. 160-61. The literature of welfare economics is
vast, but see in particular I. M. D. Little,
A Critique of Welfare Economics (London: Oxford
University Press, 1957); E. J. Mishan, Welfare Economics: Five Introductory Essays (New York: Random
House, 1964). No attempt is made in this study to
restate the postulates. For these in a natural resource context see J. Krutilla and O. Eckstein,
Multiple Purpose River Development (Baltimore:
The Johns Hopkins Press, 1958), pp. 15-51.

2. W. Kapp, The Social Costs of Private Enterprise (Cambridge: Harvard University Press,
1950; Rev. ed. 1963).

3. H. Wolozin (ed.), The Economics of Air
Pollution (New York: W. W. Norton, 1966).

4. Economists did not begin to deal with water resources in an over-all theoretical context until the early 1950's. See S. Ciriacy-Wantrup, Resource Conservation: Economics and Policies (Rev. ed.; Berkeley: University of California Division of Agricultural Sciences, 1963); Proposed Practices for Economic Analysis of River Basin Projects, Report to the Federal Inter-Agency Committee on Water Resources by its Subcommittee on Evaluation Standards (May, 1950); J. Krutilla and O. Eckstein, op. cit.; R. McKean, Efficiency in Government through Systems Analysis (New York: John Wiley & Sons, 1958); O. Eckstein, Water Resources Development: The Economics of Project Evaluation (Cambridge: Harvard University Press, 1958); J. Hirshleifer et al., Water Supply: Economics, Technology and Policy (Chicago: University of Chicago Press, 1960); A. Maass et al., Design of Water Resource Systems (Cambridge: Harvard University Press, 1962); A. Kneese, The Economics of Regional Water Quality Management (Baltimore: The Johns Hopkins Press, 1964).

5. R. Turvey, "Side Effects of Resource Use," Environmental Quality in a Growing Economy, ed. H. Jarrett (Baltimore: The Johns Hopkins Press, 1966), p. 52.

6. Maass, op. cit.; M. Meyerson and E. Banfield, Politics, Planning and the Public Interest (New York: Free Press, 1955); R. Churchman, R. Ackoff, and E. Arnoff, Introduction to Operations Research (New York: John Wiley & Sons, 1957). A slightly different formulation would be: (1) an objective or set of objectives is specified; (2) from this, a detailed and rigorous choice-criterion is formulated for use in evaluating alternative courses of action; (3) a set of alternative plans, designs, or courses of action is developed to meet the specified objectives; and (4) the alternatives are ranked in order of value by applying the choice criterion to the entire set, and the best alternative is selected.

7. For a more detailed statement, see M. Hufschmidt, "Environmental Planning," American Behavioral Scientist, X (September, 1966), 6-8.

8. Theoretically, the problem of finding an optimal system under constrained conditions can be

solved by the use of differential calculus and La-
grangean multipliers. See A. Enthoven, "The Simple
Mathematics of Maximization," an appendix in C.
Hitch and R. McKean, The Economics of Defense in
the Nuclear Age (Cambridge: Harvard University
Press, 1960). In this format, the "multiplier"
shows the marginal cost of the constraint in terms
of the costs included in the objective, i.e., an
estimate of the cost-saving that would occur if the
"standard" or constraint is reduced slightly. But
even unsophisticated techniques can be used for
making obvious comparions.

9. See M. Hufschmidt, "Field Level Planning
of Water Resource Systems," Water Resources Research, Vol. I, No. 2 (1965), pp. 147-63.

10. Kneese, op. cit., p. 199.

11. Ibid., pp. 141-45.

12. A. Kneese and B. Bower, Managing Water
Quality (Baltimore: The Johns Hopkins Press, 1968),
pp. 193-96. One can generalize by saying that, even
though constraints need to be tested for their cost
sensitivity, in the short term they are viewed as
a damage function that is perfectly inelastic at
the specified quality level and degree of certainty.

13. Hufschmidt, "Field Level Planning," op.
cit., p. 150.

14. A. C. Stern, "Basis for Criteria and Standards," Journal of the Air Pollution Control Association, XV (June, 1965), 281. A useful connection
between theory and practice is H. Wolozin, "Setting
Criteria for Public Expenditures on Air Pollution
Abatement: Theoretical Foundations and Limitations," Wolozin, op. cit., pp. 162-91.

15. U.S. Department of Health, Education and
Welfare, Air Quality Criteria for Sulfur Oxides,
Bureau of Disease Prevention and Environmental Control. (Washington, D.C.: Government Printing Office, January, 1969). Criteria on particulate
matter, photochemical oxidants, and carbon monoxide
are also available. See U.S. Senate, Air Quality
Criteria, A Staff Report of the Subcommittee on Air
and Water Pollution, Committee on Public Works, 90th
Cong., 2nd Sess., July, 1968. In terms of the formal model, the production or output-input function

expresses the relationship of air pollution damages
to pollutant concentration over time. The cost-
input function depicts the relationship of cost
(capital or OMR) to resource inputs. These costs
can be broadly classified as abatement costs. The
benefit-output function expresses the relationship
of system output (pollution reduced) to gross benefits.

16. For a more detailed discussion on the nature of standards, see A. Stern, "Summary of Existing Air Pollution Standards," Journal of the Air
Pollution Control Association, XIV (January, 1964),
5-14. There will be instances where some control
authorities will find it desirable to establish ambient air standards that are considerably more
stringent than those in other locations. For example, a community in a resort area may decide that
a degree of atmospheric clarity greater than that
achieved by most cities is essential to its economic
well-being.

17. See the case studies in Kneese and Bower,
op. cit.

3

A BROADER
DECISION-MAKING
FRAMEWORK

A useful tool for applying the welfare economist's model would be a theoretical framework that
identifies the decision points in the process of
planning and operating an air quality management
program. Because it is unrealistic to separate
economic man from political man,[1] this framework
should ideally relate economic, political, and
social behavior to the governmental structure concerned with air quality management. In other words,
the concern is with the actors in the decision process, the strategies they pursue, the nature of the
information they have available to them, and the
environment in which decisions are made.

Social scientists have developed a plethora of
overlapping, competing, and complementary theories
and models of the decision process. The literature
on the subject is vast, and only a brief review is
here attempted.[2] Examples of inclusive approaches
to decision-making include the suggestion of James
March and Herbert Simon that the processes of problem solving, politics, persuasion, and bargaining
are involved, with multiple processes combined in
the making of decisions.[3] "Disjointed incrementalism," a decision strategy involving the consideration of only a limited number of alternatives, is
seen by D. Braybrooke and C. Lindbloom as part of
a continuum of decision processes that range from
incrementalism to the rational economic model.[4]
They hold that each strategy is useful, and therefore possessing some rationality, under differing
situations with regard to the degree of change represented by the decision and the amount and certainty of information available to those making the
decisions. In like manner, Simon believes that, although social scientists have postulated a rational
decision-maker capable of choosing the alternative

that will yield the maximum possible gain, various
factors such as imperfect information result in only
"bounded rationality." For the optimizing model,
he substitutes "satisficing," which suggests that
a decision will be made when an alternative seems
to meet minimal standards, or is "good enough."[5]

More likely than finding one approach to be a
complete explanation of decision-making, the process
by which most decisions emerge is increasingly being
thought of as including multiple subprocesses.
Thus, the classic optimizing model of the economists
and Simon's "satisficing" modification of it, sometimes viewed as complete and competing explanations
of decision-making, are now regarded as "partial
theories" which might both be applied to the same
situation. For example, bargaining might take place
with other subprocesses within an optimizing framework.

Unfortunately, the specific nature of the relationship between different subprocesses of these
general decision-making systems and in the specific
case of air quality management is largely unknown
at this time. Important questions that we would
like to have answered include the following: Do
these subprocesses occur at the same time or do they
occur in sequence? In environmental management, is
there some essential activity that distinguishes
regulation from other kinds of decision processes?
What is the relative importance of the different
subprocesses in air quality management? How does
the institutional environment affect their importance? In an attempt at experimentation with different air pollution control procedures, can we
specify in detail what are the dependent and independent variables involved in optimal abatement decisions? What effect do different subprocesses have
on the objective of achieving or at least moving
toward the least-cost solution to the air pollution
problem? Answers to these questions in air quality
management call for interdisciplinary research on a
fairly large scale. Insights, however, can be
gained in the attempt to approach the minimum-cost
solution by examining the relationship of one sub-
process to cost minimization and applying the results of this examination to the study of air quality
management in a specific political and institutional
setting. Emphasis in this instance is given to the
often-mentioned role of bargaining in decision-
making.

THE ROLE OF BARGAINING

It is the belief of many social scientists
that significant public policies emerge in the political process in major part as a result of the
conflict of group interests.[6] Air quality management can be viewed as such a conflict situation
between the emitters of pollution and the air pollution control agency. In administrative theory, it
is a basic axiom that there are two ways in which
such a control agency can influence people to behave
in the desired ways, or in other words, to comply
with their policies.[7] Agencies can through education and persuasive activities seek to alter the
values or criteria employed by people in making economic choices so they will choose to act in the desired ways. Secondly, the control agency can seek
to limit the acceptable alternatives of choice available to people by attaching sanctions or penalties
to undesired alternatives or rewards or benefits to
desired alternatives.

Following the reasoning developed in the discussion of decision-making, we might reformulate this
axiom in terms of differing possible responses to
conflict over these policies. A useful reformulation
is a classification of decision-making approaches
that includes problem solving, persuasion, bargaining, and "politics".[8] Problem solving assumes that
the participants in the conflict have the same goals
but differing or incompletely developed approaches
to solving the problem and that through search and
analysis they will find a mutually satisfactory resolution to the conflict. Persuasion assumes that
the participants have common basic goals but differ
on subsidiary goals and that one participant can
convince the others to shift their less important
goals so that the conflict disappears. Bargaining
assumes persistent differences in goals but an ability to arrive at a compromise through the use of
threats, bluffing, swaps, concessions, and general
gamesmanship. Politics as a response to conflict
also implicitly assumes differences in goals among
participants but suggests that one or more of them
will expand the area of conflict so as to enlist the
aid of "outside" forces such as an appeal for arbitration in a labor dispute.[9]

The procedural forms of conflict resolution have been classified by Kenneth Boulding as reconciliation, compromise, and the award.[10] In reconciliation, the values of the parties involved change over time and they develop common preferences. In compromise, the values of the participants are not identical and there are different optimal positions for each participant in the same general area; each party, however, can be convinced to agree to a position less than his ideal rather than let the conflict last indefinitely. The third type of conflict resolution, the award, occurs when the participants agree to accept the verdict of an outside agency or party rather than let the conflict continue. In the sense that both represent less than the ideal situation for participants, the compromise and the award are very similar. The main difference is in the method of arriving at the settlement. Of all of these processes, the process of reconciliation is probably the least understood, partly due to the fact that little research has been done on it and partly because of the complexity involved.[11]

A system of appropriate procedures goes with each of these forms of conflict resolution.[12] The process of reconciliation lessens the differences of opinion between participants and is the result of discussion or argument; compromise results from a bargaining process in which conciliation and mediation probably play a considerable role; and an award is the product of legal trial or arbitration. In air quality management or in any other environmental management program, none of the three types of settlement or the various procedures should be considered as an independent technique for pollution abatement, although a tendency for one form to be more important in a particular case may be evident. Indeed, Boulding asserts that compromise and reconciliation may occur at the same time, and some reconciliation may in fact be necessary before a compromise is at all possible.[13] Therefore, it would appear that there are always likely to be elements of propaganda and discussion in bargaining situations. Similarly, in arbitration cases or in court proceedings there are often elements of bargaining and reconciliation before the award is announced. Also, the award might not be accepted unless it has been preceded by informal reconciliation and bargaining.

Compromise through bargaining is a process that can be more easily identified than the more subtle and less visible processes of value formation and change upon which reconciliation is based. Thus, the process of compromise lends itself more readily to theory construction than does reconciliation.[14]

Formal game theory has become a principal avenue for research on conflict resolution. It is briefly defined as the formal study of rational decisions in situations where "two or more individuals have choices to make, preferences regarding the outcomes, and some knowledge of the choices available to each other and of each other's preferences."[15] Bargaining which aims at finding a tolerable settlement for all participants in a conflict situation[16] falls within the theory of games but is a species of game in which relatively little progress has been made, partly because it includes situations involving common interest as well as conflict between opponents.* Cooperation is useful in this type of game because within some range of possibilities both parties will be better off with a solution, i.e., bargain, than without one. Conflict is involved because within this range of solutions the participants compete for the most favorable distribution of benefits. Thus, although both parties are interested in the adoption of some solution, they have divergent interests with regard to the particular solution that is adopted.

---

*In the terminology of game theory, bargaining is a positive-sum (as opposed to zero-sum), frequently nonsymmetrical game between participants with a mixture of conflict and cooperation. Zero-sum games are those in which one player's loss is the other's gain. The sum of gain plus loss is zero--hence "zero-sum." A positive-sum game is one in which the gain of one party is not equal to the loss of the other. For example, a gain for A of one unit of value may only cause a loss to B of one-half unit. A nonsymmetrical game results when B's loss varies from move to move even though A's gain with each move is constant. These variations from the zero-sum prototype make the mathematics of a game extremely complex. The original and still definitive source on game theory, first published in 1944 is J. von Neumann and O. Morgenstern, Theory of Games and Economic Behavior (New York: John Wiley Science Edition, 1967). A somewhat more readable account is found in R. Luce and H. Raiffa, Games and Decisions (New York: John Wiley & Sons, 1957).

Rationality and Game Theory

Because this study gives considerable emphasis to rational decision-making, it is necessary to consider the role of rationality in game theory if we are to be concerned with the relationship of bargaining to the rational model outlined earlier in this chapter. Thus, in addition to focusing on the rational pursuit of the long-run interests of society as a whole, we also need to focus on rational behavior by two or more interacting individuals or groups--in this case, governmental air pollution control agencies, business firms, public utilities, and related interest groups.

Studies of such interaction can be divided between those that attempt to examine conflict in all its complexity, without regard to whether specific behavior should be defined as either "rational or irrational," conscious or unconscious, or based on motivation or calculation, and those that focus on the more "rational," conscious, artful kind of behavior. (In discussing bargaining, L. Robbins observes that policy cannot simply be carried out "rationally" but must depend on the accommodations of people.17 The view of this study, on the other hand, is that these accommodations can be considered in a rational context.) The second type of study treats conflict as a kind of contest in which the participants are trying to "win." A study of this conscious conflict behavior is like a search for rules of optimal behavior in a contest-winning sense.

The second approach is used here because, although the concept of rationality is not necessarily the one approach that stays closest to the truth, the assumption of rational behavior is a useful one. It permits the identification of our theoretical analytical processes with those of the actual participants in a conflict. By expecting consistent behavior, we can examine alternative courses of action as to whether they met these standards of consistency. Theory that is based on the assumption that the participants "rationally" calculate their advantages according to a consistent value system allows us to think more thoroughly about the meaning of "irrationality." For example, many of the critical elements that go into a model of rational behavior can be identified with particular types of rationality or irrationality. The value system, the communication system, the information system, the collective decision process, or a parameter representing the probability of error or loss of control, can so be viewed in an effort to formalize the study of "irrationality."

Game theory is the formal study of the rational, consistent expectations that participants in a conflict situation can have about each other's choices. The concern is with situations--games of chance--in which the best course of action for each participant depends on what he expects the other participants to do, with the outcome a function of what choices are made by the other actors. The individual decision units have only partial control over the strategic factors affecting their environment since the essence of the game is the presence of adversaries whose fates are intertwined. In a fundamental sense, the phenomenon of rational agreement in this case is a psychic convergence of expectations.[18] The individual must consider how to achieve as much as possible, taking into account that there are others whose goals differ from his own and whose actions have an effect on all. Thus, the problems faced in game theory are more complex than those of simple maximization situations.

There are opposing views whether individual rationality implies joint rationality in a game theoretic analysis--the advocate of a cooperative theory may justify it by saying that people should jointly optimize, while the supporter of the noncooperative theory will say that although joint optimization might be a desirable norm, it is not necessarily reached by more or less individually rational but fallible and not particularly cooperative people. But there is agreement that in certain situations both sides can by cooperating usually agree on a solution that is more favorable to both parties than that obtained from some form of noncooperative equilibrium. The view is that individuals can gain by joint action. Thus, the John von Neumann and Oskar Morgenstern solution is an extension of welfare economics in that the rational society is presumed to select a division of proceeds that is optimal in the sense that no individual can increase his welfare by departing from it without at least one other individual suffering a decrease in his welfare.[19]

Game Theory and Bargaining

The assumption of rationality in game theory is particularly useful in a study of policy-making through bargaining because irrationality has been taken for granted by the important "pluralist" school of decision-making theorists as a necessary cost of a system that has the essential virtue of allocating power.[20] This view is in keeping with a long-standing belief in the United States that social and constitutional checks and balances serve not to promote efficiency but to preclude the exercise of arbitrary power.[21] Thus, although bargaining is often mentioned in any review of approaches to decision-making, it is not always clear, as Roland McKean has pointed out, just how bargaining works.[22] In other words, its impact on some defined optimal solution is not known. Because of this lack of knowledge, bargaining is at best often viewed as a constraint in decision-making rather than a variable that might be manipulated. Richard Cyert's explanation for this phenomenon is that in the making of public economic policy, uncertainty results in few generally accepted operational criteria for determining economic efficiency, that there are many competing groups with diverse interests and values seeking to influence policy making so that clear objectives cannot be established, and that a variety of other political, social, and ethical as well as economic considerations are involved in the making of such policies.[23] Consequently, the policy process is said to involve the striking of balances, not the choice between "right" and "wrong" in any absolute sense that can be anticipated ahead of time.

Strictly speaking, game theory is not predictive. It is what is sometimes called normative theory in contrast to predictive or explanatory theory. It might also be called "vicarious problem solving," an approach that has been traditional in economics and is useful in the same sense that the assumption of profit maximization is useful.[24] In this sense, it can be used to help discover the attributes of alternative strategies for achieving these solutions. Within the game theoretic framework, bargaining is not viewed as a constraint within which one attempts to optimize. Using the framework, understanding can be gained on how bargaining operates. Such understanding is a necessary precondition for relating

bargaining to the formal rational decision model
which deals with objectives, criteria, standards,
and plan implementation.

Limitations on the Use of Game Theory

Although he does not use the term "rational,"
McKean believes that the bargaining mechanism leads
to a pattern of decisions that is "somewhat orderly
and sensible."[25] His view is that if a public official's action will use up someone's property or
damage certain interests, the official will probably
find a cost associated with that action. He will
feel the complaints of those damaged or the incon-
venience of trying to mollify them, or he may suffer
embarrassing or expensive enmities among his col-
leagues or retaliation by other affected parties.
McKean continues that this official has to bargain
with many people who are affected and, in one way or
another, encounter costs if he makes decisions that
impose sacrifices on others. From those who are
benefited, on the other hand, he can bargain for
compensation, with the reward possibly being support
in connection with some other matter, reduced en-
mity, increased friendship, or convenience. The
size and completeness of the compensations for both
costs inflicted and gains bestowed depend upon bargaining strengths and circumstances; shifts in these
costs and gains cause shifts in behavior. McKean
concludes that "the greater the extent to which
these compensations are made, the less the extent
to which the costs and gains felt by an official
will diverge from total costs and gains."

His view of costs and gains is fundamentally a
psychic one--some of the costs he mentions cannot
easily be fitted in with a quest for the monetary
minimum-cost solution to pollution abatement. In
like manner, in game theory the phenomenon of rational agreement is a fundamentally psychic convergence of expectations. Thus a basic difficulty--at
least for our purposes--with behavior in game theory
situations is that in general each player's strategy
will depend on his expectations about the other
player's strategies. A basic weakness of formal
game theory for analyzing social situations is its
failure to consider that in the general situation
of decision-making under uncertainty, we not only

face some degree of uncertainty as to the strategies of the opponent but great uncertainty as to the payoffs themselves. For example, one's perception of alternative payoffs and strategies is crucially affected by previous experience, but experience is not incorporated in formal game theory.

Could we assume that a player's expectations were given, then his problem of strategy choice would become a strategy maximizing his own payoff on the assumption that the other players would act in accordance with his given expectations. But the point is that game theory cannot regard the players' expectations about each other's behavior as given; rather, one of the most important problems for game theory is precisely to decide what expectations players can entertain about other intelligent players' behavior. This is called the problem of mutual "rational expectations."[26] As Kenneth Boulding has pointed out, the distinction between rational and irrational behavior in game theory lies in the degree of "stability of the images" involved rather than in any distinction of the principle of the optimum.[27] There is, thus, no best choice independently defined ahead of time such as is found in a welfare solution even though the solution to the game would be considered optimal upon completion of the series of moves that result in the outcome. Schelling suggests that nonzero-sum game theory may have missed its most promising field by being pitched at too abstract a level of analysis.[28] He believes that by abstracting from communication and enforcement systems knowledge related to alternatives and payoffs associated with them, and by treating the players as identical (in perfect symmetry), game theory has overshot the level at which the most fruitful work could be done and has defined away some of the essential ingredients of typical nonzero-sum games. Preoccupied with the solution to "the" nonzero-sum game, game theory, he states, has not done justice to some typical game situations or game models and to the "moves" that are peculiar to nonzero-sum games of strategy.[29]

Another criticism is that the possibility that words or statements might be used as moves in a game is expressly avoided in all formal game theory analysis. Moves are conceived of as physical acts such as producing a good for the market. In the original

work of von Neumann and Morgenstern, it is specifically stated that the verbal bargaining, haggling,
and discussion among players--the dynamics of coming
to an agreement--are excluded from the analysis.[30]
Thus, suggestions and inferences, threats and promises are of no consequence in the accepted formal
theory of games. But when we come to matters of
negotiation, words play a critical role as moves
whether they be in the form of threats, bluffs, or
statements in the news media. Game theory has not
successfully been able to solve the coding problem
of relating words to acts. The limitations of game
theory have served to clarify the problem, but no
solution has yet been supplied.

Due to these inherent characteristics, it now
appears to many that the conceptual and rudimentary
aspects of game theory are the most valuable to the
social scientist.[31] Rather than being thought of
as a formal "theory," it is now viewed as a framework for analysis that can be adapted and modified
according to specific needs. In essence, game theory provides a point of reference for examining a
problem and gaining insights without accepting the
often unrealistic rules of the game. With this in
mind, the following sections rely on the general
framework of game theory and the results of game
theoretic research as a basis for examining decision-
making in air quality management.

Useful Terminology

Research on conflict resolution has produced a
set of terms for describing the actors and behavior
involved in conflict situations. Although there is
no definitive vocabulary, some of the more commonly
used terms are as follows.[32] A behavior unit may be
a person, a family, or a social organization such
as a firm. It becomes a party or participant when
it becomes involved in conflict with another behavior
unit. A position of a behavior unit at any point in
time is defined by a set of variables or values that
defines this unit. The history of a unit is the record of positions it has occupied at successive points
in time.

Competition exists when the actual or potential positions of two behavior units are mutually

incompatible. This is a broader concept than conflict
in that all cases of conflict involve competition
while not all cases of competition involve conflict.
Conflict exists as a situation of competition when
the parties are aware of the incompatibility or potential positions--each party wishes to occupy a position that is incompatible with the wishes of the
other. A strategy is a rule of choice or general
plan of action containing instructions as to what to
do in every contingency.* The payoff function of a
party is his evaluation of all outcomes of the game.
A game is described in terms of the players or individual decision-makers, the payoffs or the values
assigned to the outcomes of the game, the rules
specifying the variables that each player controls,
the information conditions, and all other relevant
aspects of the decision environment.

Somewhat less common but still very useful terminology includes the following. The bargaining
range, bargaining field, or contract zone represents
the joint universe of alternative positions. A
boundary of possibility defines certain limitations
on the positions imposed by various physical, psychological, legal, and monetary restrictions. From
conflict points, it is not possible to make a move
that makes both parties better off--any move would
make at least one party worse off. These points
constitute the conflict set.[33] Conflict moves are
made from these points. Moves that make both parties
better off are called trading moves. Within a set
of trading moves, it is possible for one party to
give up something in return for something else that
will benefit both parties. A process of trading
leads to the conflict set.

Minimum dispositions of parties are the lower
limits of a bargaining range. Often, however, minimum dispositions and the bargaining range are not
estimated by participants since they feel such an

---

*Most people do not appear to use the concept
of strategy consciously, as understood in game theory, in their planning and decision-making. Many
tend to "play by ear" rather than plan in detail.
It is the belief of students of game theory and decision theory that individuals should consciously
attempt at least to consider their problems in terms
of alternative strategies.

act might reduce flexibility and the capacity to put pressure on their opponent.[34] Also, in complex conflicts a number of bargaining ranges might be combined in an over-all bargain. Therefore, instead of estimating a bargaining range, a party may estimate a probable outcome, i.e., the approximate terms at which he expects agreement.

A position in a range or field is acceptable to one of the parties if he is willing to conclude a bargain at this position. A field can be divided into an acceptable set and a nonacceptable set by a boundary of acceptability for each party. If the acceptable sets do not overlap--have no common points--no bargain can be struck. Finally, there is the objective situation as might be seen by an omniscient outside observer and the situation of the first party as perceived by the second, and of the second as perceived by the first. Due to possible misunderstandings, the behavior of a party depends not on the objective situation but on its perception of itself and the opponent.

Bargaining Research

Continuous Games

Research on conflict situations clearly shows that negotiation and bargaining operate best in situations where the subject in contention can be divided into parts that can be dealt with sequentially, preferably over an indeterminate period of time. This incrementalism, whether achieved by changes in moves or in value systems, is of considerable importance.[35] (In any one game, the incrementalism of the moves may be more important than the incrementalism in the value systems and vice versa.) To draw the analogy of chess, players move in turn, each moving a piece at a time; the game proceeds at a slow tempo by small increments and is of an indeterminate length. The game changes character in the course of play by a succession of small changes that can be observed and appreciated, with plenty of time allowed for mistakes of individual players or mutual mistakes to be noticed and adapted to in later play. In an uncertain situation, a person is often saved from making a strategic error if he defers a decision in order that the capacity to make future decisions is not relinquished.[36] Thus, sophisticated

decision procedures are not preferred since they may
lead to premature closure, to too little emphasis on
hesitation and liquidity, and hence possibly to
major mistakes.[37]

Development of Trust

The decomposition or issue-division tactic in
bargaining can be applied to either threats or to
promises, and can be viewed as a necessary prere-
quisite for making a bargain enforceable. This is
so because there is a perception on the part of the
participants that future possibilities for agreement
will not develop unless mutual trust is created and
maintained. The participants need to be confident
that each of them will not jeopardize opportunities
for future agreement by destroying mutual trust near
the start of a period of interaction which is defined as the game.[38] Such confidence is naturally
not always in evidence, so decomposition serves to
encourage the same expectations on the part of all
participants.

The Learning Process

An aspect of building mutual expectations is
that if a threat can be decomposed into a series of
consecutive threats, there is an opportunity to demonstrate to an opponent during his initial reaction
to a threat that you "mean business," thereby making
the continuous game a learning experience.[39] Thus,
credibility can be developed as trust is being created.

The Role of Rituals

Another aspect of the continuous game which must
be considered is that negotiating processes develop
certain rituals, and attempts to by-pass or reduce
these rituals may destroy the negotiating process
itself.[40] For example, the parties may begin the
proceedings with somewhat bombastic statements that
set the initial boundaries to the negotiations.
There is a period of withdrawal designed to make it
appear that the commitments are genuine. The parties know, however, that the commitments are not
absolute; otherwise, the negotiations would break
down. There may follow a process of trading by
which mutual concessions are made, and there may
have to be a period during which, even though no
visible progress occurs, the incipient settlement is

in fact developing. The resolution of conflict
through bargaining thus involves the difficult institutional problem of arranging these ritual elements in the proper order and proportion.[41] Because
legal procedures may be too inflexible to permit the
proper mix of ritual elements required by the bargaining and reconciling processes, a formal legal
proceeding may often be a poor way of handling a
conflict in air pollution control.[42]

Commitment

Schelling has pointed out the great advantage
that an irrevocable commitment gives a bargainer,
provided that it does not preclude the possibility
of any bargain at all.[43] This leads to the paradox
that the weakest bargainer is frequently in the
strongest bargaining position, as his very weakness
gives him a commitment that would be taken away by
strength. The weak have nowhere to go, no place to
which to retreat, and their very weakness makes
their bargaining commitments irrevocable.

It is thus useful for participants to reduce
the scope of their authority or by other means reduce the alternatives available to them. But if
one can demonstrate to an opponent that he is not
strongly committed to a position or has miscalcu-
lated his commitment, one may in fact undo or revise
this commitment. Another approach is to confuse
the opponent's commitment so that his constituents
or audience cannot easily identify how the commitment is to be complied with. This may undo or lower
the value of the commitment. In such cases, it is
to an opponent's obvious disadvantage if his commitment can be successfully refuted by argument.

When an opponent has resolved to make a concession, a party can help him by showing that he can
make a moderate concession consistent with his former position, and that if he does this there is no
basis for thinking that this reflects on his basic
principles. Basic to this strategy is that one
denies oneself too great an award from the opponent's concession or the concession will not be made.

Reputation Value

A potent means of commitment, and sometimes
the only means, is to emphasize the importance of
maintaining one's reputation.[44] It is to the

advantage of a participant if he can persuasively
point to an array of other negotiations in which
his own position would be prejudiced if he made a
concession in this instance.

The Prominent Solution

Most bargaining situations in the final analysis involve some range of possible solutions within
which the parties involved would rather make a concession than fail to reach any agreement. In such
a situation, there are potential outcomes from which
one or both parties will be willing to retreat for
the sake of reaching an agreement, and often the
other party knows what these are. Each party's
strategy is guided by what he expects the other to
accept or insist upon, and each knows that the other
is guided by reciprocal thoughts. The final outcome
is at a point from which neither expects the other
to retreat. These reflexive expectations converge
on a single point at which each participant expects
his opponent "not to expect to be expected to retreat."[45]

This behavior results in considerable importance being given to "salient," "focal point," or
prominent solutions.[46] Such a solution has characteristics that distinguish it qualitatively from
surrounding alternatives. These characteristics
might be related to a perception by the participants
of the historical, cultural, legal, and moral properties of the situation which serve to focus expectations on certain solutions. For example, even in
situations where the possible outcome of a bargain
is its evident "fairness" in terms of the standards
that the participants are known to appreciate,
Schelling argues that the moral aspects of a fair
solution are reinforced by the ability of this solution to focus attention on itself.[47] Similarly,
he notes that when the weight of public opinion
seems to influence the participants to decide on an
obviously "fair" or "reasonable" outcome, one can
give too much emphasis or even possibly not under-
stand the manner in which public opinion influences
the parties in the game unless credit is given to
its ability to develop mutual expectations.

If a party holds out for a solution that is
not prominent, there is a danger of no settlement
at all. Hence, given a choice between a high

probability of reaching an agreement at a salient
point and a low probability of reaching a settlement
at a point which would be more favorable to him,
each party tends to choose the salient point having
the maximum expected value. Another attraction of
a focal point is that if one starts to make small
concessions, these can open the door to much larger
ones. After a participant has forsaken a principle
in some obvious manner, there can seemingly be no
stopping point to further concessions. If one is
about to make a concession, he needs to control his
adversary's expectations in that he needs a recog-
nizable limit to his retreat. And if one is to make
a finite concession that is not to be interpreted
as a capitulation, he needs an obvious place to
stop. As Schelling notes:

> If we then ask what it is that can
> bring their expectations into conver-
> gence and bring the negotiation to a
> close, we might propose that it is
> the intrinsic magnetism of particular
> outcomes, especially those that enjoy
> prominence, uniqueness, simplicity,
> precedent, or some rationale that
> makes them qualitatively differenti-
> able from the continuum of possible
> alternatives. We could argue that
> expectations tend not to converge on
> outcomes that differ only by degree
> from alternative outcomes but that
> people have to dig in their heels at
> a groove in order to make any show
> of determination. One has to have a
> reason for standing firmly on a po-
> sition; and along the continuum of
> qualitatively undifferentiable posi-
> tions one finds no rationale. The
> rationale may not be strong at the
> arbitrary 'focal point' but at least
> it can defend itself with the argu-
> ment 'If not here, where?'[48]

The Role of Precedent

It has also been found that there is a remark-
able frequency with which long negotiation over complicated quantitative formulas or shares in some
benefits and costs are ultimately influenced by a
seemingly irrelevant previous negotiation. Precedent

seems to exercise an influence that considerably exceeds its logical importance.[49] Past bargains become precedents for present situations in that they often remove from conscious consideration many agreements, decisions, and commitments that might well be subject to renegotiation as conditions change.

Mathematical Simplicity

In bargains that involve quantification of solutions, there seems to be some appeal in mathematical simplicity. Outcomes are favored that can be expressed in even numbers since they provide good "resting places." Thus, a compromise at 47 per cent is much less likely than at 50 per cent. In general, though, the numerical scale is too continuous to provide strong focal points. Thus, saliency generally depends on qualitative principles. But a commitment to a principle that provides the basis for a numerical calculation that comes out at a specific number may provide the support for a stand at that point.

Conclusions on Bargaining Research

Several aspects of the many facets of bargaining have been reviewed, including incrementalism, ritualization, continuing negotiation, and focal point solutions. They suggest that rationality in bargaining outcomes is a function of basically psychic phenomena. At first, this view may appear to run contrary to the accepted economic notion that "rationality" is evident only in the minimum-cost solution. But a broader view of decision-making may suggest that the least-cost solution is most readily approximated through procedures that take full cognizance of the psychic elements in any bargaining situation and channel these elements in the direction of a mutually sought, economically sound goal.

Some intuitive conclusions come to mind. For example, a semblance of a continuing game can be created by separating the issue at stake into consecutive components. This is a concern of some importance in environmental management situations since they are structurally "lumpier" than chess games. In air pollution control, there is often no continuous range of choices open to the polluter and

the abatement officer. Due to the initial administrative and psychic costs and the initial and
marginal capital costs, moves have a considerable
impact, and it is usually difficult to project a
control situation more than a move or two ahead because of the uncertainties involved. The pace of
the game can bring things to a head before much experience has been gained or much of an understanding
has been reached, unless ways are found to increase
the number of possible moves. The use of incrementalism in structuring pollution abatement progress
eases the impact of each move and allows the participants to acquire both knowledge of each other
and experience with the particular problem at hand.
Psychic and monetary costs to the participants are
spread over a longer period of time, and the slower
pace of the process and the indeterminate length of
the "game" reduce the possibility of crisis. Because
of these advantages gained through the use of incrementalism, one would expect that conscious attempts would be made to increase the number of
"moves" and extend the life of the game. It is of
interest that the Air Quality Act of 1967 specifies
that multiple actions must take place before final
regulatory action occurs. These steps make the process more incremental in nature, thus gaining for
the participants the advantages described above.

     Bargaining research suggests that both the act
to be deterred and the punishment must be divisible.
The threatening party (the air pollution control
agency) in certain situations may not be able to di-
vide the act into steps. However, the principle
remains that it is poor strategy to require compliance in terms of some critical amount or degree that
would be deemed mandatory, for action geared to increments has a greater chance of success than one
that must be carried out on an all-or-nothing basis.

     At first glance, we might also conclude that if
the outcome of a game is seemingly already determined by the participants' perception of the config-
uration of the problem itself and where the focal
point lies, the scope of bargaining skill would be
insignificant. But it can be argued that what the
participants' perception does is shift the locus
where skill is important. The prominent solution
depends greatly on how the problem is formulated, on
what analogies or precedents the definition of the
bargaining issue calls to mind, and on the kinds of

data that may be available to bring to bear on the
question in dispute. Thus, bargaining skill in air
pollution control can be seen to be important not
only during a bargaining session, but also before
actual bargaining begins by being able to give prominence to some particular outcomes that would be
favorable to a participant's point of view.

BARGAINING AND AIR POLLUTION CONTROL

In the United States today, there are receptors
of the air resource and emitters of pollutants who use
the air as a waste disposal and transmittal medium.
The receptor receives free a volume of air on which
he places a positive value, whereas the emitter is
given a good (the waste disposal capacity of the
air) which has a positive value for him but a negative value for the receptor. Neither party pos-
sesses a way of resolving this conflict to his
satisfaction other than attempting to convince the
public and its designated representatives of the
dire consequences of reducing or not increasing
the availability of that dimension of the air which
to him is the most valuable. In this situation, it
is useful for emitters of air pollution to complain
about unproductive investment in air pollution abatement and control equipment and, at the same time,
it is worthwhile for receptors to complain about the
lack of clean air.

This problem seems amenable to study using the
bargaining framework and research conclusions detailed above, for selected experience in air quality
management is now available. The hypothesis that
rational decision-making procedures that allow for
bargaining behavior will reduce both uncertainty and
costs in the long run can therefore be given at
least initial examination.

Because a detailed analysis of this theoretical
question is--and must be--related to actual experiences in air quality management in the United
States, important considerations are the political
and institutional framework outlined in Chapter 1,
the technical nature of the problem, and the adopted
approach to control. These latter two considerations
should be thought of as defining the "rules of the
game" within which decisions can be made. The nature

of these decision rules are spelled out in the next
chapter.

NOTES

1. S. Marglin, "The Social Rate of Discount
and the Optimal Rate of Investment," Quarterly Journal of Economics, LXXVII (February, 1963), 99.
Bolan's variables that need to be accounted for in
the city planning process are pertinent here. These
include the character of the issue-generating forces,
the character of the decisions to be made, the his-
torical-social context, the decision-making framework, the dynamics of decision-making, the planning
strategy, the planning method, the planning program
content, and the position of the planning decision
system in the governmental framework. R. Bolan,
"Emerging Views of Planning," Journal of the American Institute of Planners, XXXIII (July, 1967),
233-45.

2. For a useful review of the major contributions in the area of decision theory, see J. Robinson and R. Majak, "The Theory of Decision-Making,"
Contemporary Political Analysis, ed. J. Charlesworth
(New York: Free Press, 1967), 175-88; and Bolan,
op. cit.

3. J. March and H. Simon, Organizations (New
York: John Wiley & Sons, 1958), 129-31.

4. D. Braybrooke and C. Lindbloom, A Strategy
for Decision (New York: Free Press, 1964).

5. H. Simon, Models of Man (New York: John
Wiley & Sons, 1957). In addition to the article by
Robinson and Majak, op. cit., a similar statement
of this view is E. Etzioni, "Mixed Scanning: A
Third Approach to Decision-Making," Public Administration Review, XXVII (December, 1967), 385-92.
Robinson and Majak's classification of subprocesses
distinguishes among intellectual, social, and
"quasi-mechanical" aspects of decision-making.
These include optimizing, "satisficing," coalition
formation, interest group interaction, interest ag-
gregation, bargaining, the price mechanism, overlapping games, among others.

6. For example, see J. Anderson, Politics and the Economy (Boston: Little, Brown, 1966); M. Olson, The Logic of Collective Action (New York: Schocken Books, 1968), Ch. 5. H. Wolozin suggests that economic market decisions be viewed as conflict and that economic decision models be expanded by illustrating what can be done to incorporate certain psychological findings on the role of will and willfulness into the theory of economic decision and behavior. H. Wolozin, "Intransigent Economic Behavior in Air Pollution Control and Economic Decision" (Paper presented at the Air Pollution Control Association Conference, Cleveland, Ohio, June, 1967).

7. H. Simon, Administrative Behavior (New York: Free Press, 1965).

8. March and Simon, op. cit., 129-31.

9. Ibid.

10. K. Boulding, Conflict and Defense: A General Theory (New York: Harper, 1962), 309-10.

11. Ibid., p. 310. Much of the work in this area is being done by psychologists. See D. Summer, "Conflict, Compromise, and Belief Change in a Decision-Making Task," Journal of Conflict Resolution, XII (June, 1968) 215-21.

12. Boulding, op. cit.

13. Ibid., p. 311.

14. Ibid., p. 313. For a first attempt, see M. Holden, Pollution Control as a Bargaining Process: An Essay on Regulatory Decision-Making (Ithaca, N.Y.: Cornell University Water Resources Center, October, 1966).

15. T. Schelling, "What is Game Theory?" Contemporary Political Analysis, ed. J. Charlesworth (New York: Free Press, 1967), p. 213. There are available well over a thousand books and articles dealing with game theory. For the main sources, see the bibliography in M. Shubik (ed.), Game Theory and Related Approaches to Social Behavior (New York: John Wiley & Sons, 1964), 363-76.

16. E. Banfield, "Notes on a Conceptual Scheme," in M. Meyerson and E. Banfield, Politics, Planning

and the Public Interest (New York: Free Press, 1964), p. 307.

17. L. Robbins, Politics and Economics: Papers in Political Economy (New York: St. Martin's Press, 1963), pp. 20-21.

18. T. Schelling, The Strategy of Conflict (New York: Oxford University Press, 1963) p. 114. For examples of the use of rationality postulates in formal game theory analysis, see J. Harsanyi, "A General Theory of Rational Behavior in Game Situations," Econometrica, XXXIII (July, 1966), 613-34; J. Harsanyi, "On the Rationality Postulates Underlying the Theory of Cooperative Games," Journal of Conflict Resolution, V (June, 1961), 179-96.

19. J. von Neumann and O. Morgenstern, Theory of Games and Economic Behavior (New York: John Wiley Science Edition, 1967). This should not be confused with a "fair" solution in terms of some moral criteria as used by Anscombe and Raiffa. F. Anscombe and R. Aumann, in "A Definition of Subjective Probability," Annals of Mathematical Statistics, XXXIV (1963), 199-205; H. Raiffa, "Arbitration Schemes for Generalized Two-Person Games," Contributions to the Theory of Games, ed. H. Kuhn and A. Tucker (Princeton, N.J.: Princeton University Press, 1954), Vol. II, Ch. 21.

20. For a discussion of pluralism, see Robinson and Majak, op. cit.

21. H. Kariel, The Decline of American Pluralism (Stanford, Calif.: Stanford University Press, 1961).

22. R. McKean, "The Unseen Hand in Government," American Economic Review, LXXIX (June, 1965), 494.

23. R. Cyert and J. March, A Behavioral Theory of the Firm (Englewood Cliffs, N.J.: Prentice-Hall, 1967), p. 31. In terms of the earlier rational decision model, bargaining would be considered a formal constraint within which one seeks to maximize the objective function. For a comparison of the two normative theories, see M. Shubik, Competition, Oligopoly, and the Theory of Games (Princeton, N.J.: Princeton University Press, 1958).

24. McKean, op. cit., p. 498.

25. Ibid. For another view of the role of costs in political choice, see J. Buchanan and G. Tullock, The Calculus of Consent (Ann Arbor: University of Michigan Press, 1962).

26. Harsanyi, "On the Rationality of Postulates Underlying the Theory of Cooperative Games," op. cit.

27. Boulding, op. cit., p. 215. Game theory assumes the existence of a real utility for each player which is stable throughout the game. Each player knows his own utility and that of all the other players eventually.

28. T. Schelling, The Strategy of Conflict, op. cit., p. 119. He also argues (p. 114) that if the phenomenon of rational agreement is a psychic convergence of expectations there is no presumption that mathematical game theory is essential to the process of reaching agreement, hence there is no basis for presuming that mathematics is a main source of inspiration in the convergence process.

29. Boulding, op. cit., p. 215.

30. Von Neumann and Morgenstern, op. cit., Ch. 1. Suggestions and inferences, threats and promises are of no consequence in the accepted theory of games because they imply a relation between the two players that must be to the disadvantage of one player; and he can destroy it by adopting a "minimax" strategy whereby one adopts a position in which one minimizes maximum loss rather than try to maximize gain. See A. Koo, "Recurrent Objections to the Minimax Strategy," Review of Economics and Statistics, XLI (February, 1959), 36-43.

31. Schelling, "What is Game Theory?", op. cit., p. 219. Shubik, "The Uses of Game Theory," Contemporary Political Analysis, ed. J. Charlesworth (New York: Free Press, 1967), p. 260; A. Rapoport, Fights, Games and Debates (Ann Arbor: University of Michigan Press, 1960).

32. This terminology has been drawn from the following representative sources: Boulding, op. cit., pp. 2-18; Shubik, Game Theory and Related Approaches to Social Behavior, op. cit., pp. 8-14;

C. Stevens, Strategy and Collective Bargaining Negotiation (New York: McGraw Hill, 1963), pp. 9-56.

33. The analogy here is to the Edgeworth contract curve in economics. See Boulding, op. cit., p. 15.

34. F. Ikle and N. Leites, "Political Negotiation as a Process of Modifying Utilities," Journal of Conflict Resolution, VI (March, 1962), 19-28.

35. Schelling, The Strategy of Conflict, op. cit., p. 170.

36. K. Boulding, The Impact of the Social Sciences (New Brunswick, N.J.: Rutgers University Press, 1966), p. 43. In formal game theory, the one who makes a choice first in a way the other participant can see will lose the game no matter what he chooses. This fact points to the value of postponing decisions, of gaining intelligence about the choice another has already made, and denying intelligence in case one has to move first.

37. Richard Cyert's studies of industrial firms suggest that firms avoid uncertainty by using procedures that minimize the need for predicting uncertain future events such as using short-run feedback as a trigger for action. R. Cyert and J. March, op. cit.

38. Schelling, The Strategy of Conflict, op. cit., p. 45. This would seem to be particularly applicable to negotiations between firms and governmental regulatory agencies.

39. The learning process is detailed in A. Rapoport and A. M. Ghammah, Prisoner's Dilemma (Ann Arbor: University of Michigan Press, 1965). Learning models such as those noted by Rapoport and behavioral models as sketched by March and Simon, op. cit., and Ikle op. cit., are as relevant to the study of conflict as game theory.

40. A. Douglas, "The Peaceful Settlement of Industrial and Intergroup Disputes," Journal of Conflict Resolution, I (March, 1957), p. 69. Also see A. Douglas, Industrial Peacemaking (New York: Columbia University Press, 1962); L. Randolph, "A Suggested Model of International Negotiation,"

Journal of Conflict Resolution, X (September, 1966)
344-53; Stevens, op. cit.

41.   Boulding, op. cit., p. 311.

42.   Ibid., p. 313.

43.   Schelling, The Strategy of Conflict, op.
cit., p. 34.

44.   Ibid., p. 30.

45.   R. Willis and M. Joseph, "Prominence as a
Predictor of the Outcome of Games of Agreement,"
Journal of Conflict Resolution, IV (June, 1959),
102-13; Schelling, The Strategy of Conflict, op.
cit., pp. 69-72.

46.   J. Stone, "An Experiment in Bargaining
Games," Econometrica, XXVI (August, 1958), 286-96;
Schelling, Strategy of Conflict, op. cit., pp. 111-
13.

47.   Schelling, The Strategy of Conflict, op.
cit., p. 72.

48.   Ibid, p. 70.

49.   R. Cyert and J. March, A Behavioral Theory
of the Firm, op. cit., p. 33.

CHAPTER APPROACHES TO
AIR POLLUTION
ABATEMENT

Air pollution control is largely a matter of
reducing or eliminating pollutants coming from a
source, eliminating the activity that is the source,
shifting the location of the source or the recipient, or changing the timing of release of emissions.
Although the latter three solutions are sometimes
used, a major across-the-board emphasis is given
to reducing levels of pollutant emissions. Stationary sources can be controlled by changes in process,
either in manufacturing or combustion, utilizing
more efficient equipment, substituting raw materials
used in the process, changing fuels, and operating
and maintaining existing equipment at the point of
emission into the atmosphere.[1] These control procedures can operate either singly or in combination,
the specific procedures depending on the source to
be controlled.

Representative examples of control procedures
include the following. Abatement of emissions from
space heating is based on a shift from high-sulphur
coal and oil to low-sulfur oil and natural gas and
more efficient combustion processes. Refuse incineration emissions are being abated by controlled
high-temperature, multichamber furnaces with auxiliary fuel injection, installation of dust control
apparatus, and high maintenance standards. Industrial emissions from the petroleum industry, electric power plants, and metallurgical and chemical
processes are caused by combustion inefficiency, fuel
content, product leakage and evaporation, and inadequate air and gas cleaning devices. Thus, a mix of
abatement procedures is used. In general, however,
most attention has been given by control agencies to
changes in fuel use and to installation of recovery
equipment such as electrostatic precipitators and
mechanical cleaners at the point of emission.[2]

APPROACHES TO REGULATION

These techniques for pollution abatement can be applied by relying on one or a combination of three approaches to environmental quality management-- direct regulation, the use of effluent fees, and payments.[3] Direct regulation includes a combination of licenses, permits, registration, zoning, air quality and effluent standards, and the enforcement of standards through regulatory bodies and the courts. The effluent fee approach involves assessing a monetary charge on emitters based on the amount of pollution they emit. The payments approach is the obverse: providing subsidies or tax abatements as incentives for polluters to reduce pollution at the source. Common examples include the subsidization of particular control equipment and accelerated depreciation and tax credits for investment in control equipment.

Direct Regulation

The most common method for dealing with problems of air pollution is direct regulation of emissions.[4] One aspect of such regulation is the use of zoning powers.* Another example is seen in existing Department of Health, Education and Welfare policies on air pollution abatement, which most often fall in the category of regulation and enforcement activities.[5] A considerable advantage of this approach is that it permits the government to take

---

*With respect to primary pollutants, the particulates and other pollutants that do not change in the air and which have a relatively short fallout potential, the objective of zoning is the physical separation of emitter and receptors. This is most important in the location of major public facilities such as power plants and major industrial uses whose location can usually be affected by zoning controls. But zoning without some type of emission controls may protect adjacent residents from immediate concentrations while the over-all levels of air pollution in the metropolitan area continue to rise. Placing factories down-wind of residences is inadequate for coping with the problem of photochemical smog.

interim steps even though it has little information on relevant measurements. For example, if people's eyes were burning because of the plumes from an industrial plant, it would be logical to require abatement of these emissions even if ways of measuring the plant's contribution to over-all levels of pollution in the air were not considered accurate, and even if the detailed effect of these over-all levels on health could not be specified. Such regulation by a governmental agency operating in the public interest is justified by government officials relying on the public health argument that suspected negative health effects from air pollution are sufficient basis for abatement action.[6] A similar argument for regulation using inadequate data that emphasizes monetary costs finds support in a recent staff report of the Committee on Public Works of the U.S. Senate, which states: "Whatever yardsticks are employed, it is clearly evident that the cost of property damages alone from air pollution is great--far greater than the amounts devoted to its abatement by industry and all levels of government."[7] The implication of this often-heard argument seems to be that there is little chance of the costs of such a program of direct regulation exceeding the benefits.

Proponents of direct regulation also emphasize its effectiveness; regulations are easy to administer and noncompliance can easily be determined. Direct regulation is also considered to be equitable, at least superficially, in that all polluters must comply with the same regulation even though the costs they would face might vary significantly.

Not all economists view direct regulation with complete suspicion. Thomas Crocker states:

> Given the uncertain quality of available physical, biological, and economic information, and the potentially high costs associated with the gathering of additional information about atmospheric pollution problems, the control authority, in order to impress receptors and emitters with the necessity of regarding the air's two value dimensions as scarce economic resources, appears to be justified in setting minimum standards.[8]

A greater commitment to emission standards is evident in the writings of Paul Gerhardt, an economist with the National Air Pollution Control Administration. He states:

> A polluter faced with the necessity
> to comply with a law or suffer punish-
> ment will generally find the least
> cost set of controls or have no one
> to blame but himself. He will pass
> cost increases along to customers in
> the form of reduced profit shares.
> Optimum allocation will be preserved
> as the public makes new choices about
> their spending and investing patterns.
> Administrative costs could be less
> than for some alternatives as there
> would be no complicated tax revenue
> emission charge or payment system
> to operate.[9]

He argues that continuous direct regulation provides continuing incentives to minimize the cost of abatement in much the same manner that effluent fees do. If a firm is restricted only in the amount of pollution it can emit, a continuing search would most likely be made for the minimum cost of accomplishing this.[10]

But, as expected, relative simplicity is not achieved without certain costs. Although direct regulation may be reasonably effective in dealing with the grossest forms of pollution, it may be difficult to use for equalizing incremental abatement costs among emitters in a relatively precise manner. Thus, one objection to direct regulation is its alleged inflexibility which results in considerably higher costs than would more selective abatement. Although it can be argued with justification that direct regulation can be administered in a flexible manner, experiences to date in the water resources field shows that certain procedures easily become institutionalized and prove very difficult to change. An example of the costs involved has been pointed out by the Federal Water Pollution Control Administration, which found in the Delaware River Basin that simple equal-proportional reduction of all waste loads--a form of direct regulation--would cost 50 per cent more than achieving the same quality standard by requiring firms to reduce their waste loads in proportion to their

harmful effects.[11] In the case of air quality management, the Federal Coordinating Committee on the
Economic Impact of Pollution Abatement suggests that
the cost of achieving a specific air quality standard could increase by 200 to 400 per cent if equal-
proportional reduction on a year-round basis is
proposed.[12]

Effluent Fees

Most economists believe that the objective of
pollution abatement programs should be to minimize
the total of (a) air pollution damage costs and (b)
the costs incurred in any program to alleviate that
damage. Accordingly, any given level of pollution
abatement should be reached by the least costly
combination of means available, and the costs of
any decrement of pollution should not exceed the
benefits obtained by the reduction. Thus, the common effluent fee approach would be to calculate the
damage to each receptor from polluted air containing
various amounts and kinds of effluents. Such a
calculation would permit measurement of the benefits to be expected from proposed abatement projects.
Next, one would calculate the cost to each pollutant source of abating its emissions in varying de-
grees--recognizing that the smaller the amount of
pollutant discharged, the greater the abatement
costs will be to the source. The optimal allocation
of the air resource would then require that pollutants be prevented from entering the atmosphere at
levels that would inflict more marginal damage on
receptors than the marginal cost to the source of
preventing the pollution.[13]

The operational procedure followed would include an evaluation of the damage done by the emission of incremental amounts of pollutant into the
air at any given location and time and an assessment
of a corresponding charge against the emitters. The
charge would reflect the marginal cost that the
sources impose on others and would be determined by
relating ambient air quality to rates of emission
using air-monitoring networks and relatively simple
atmospheric diffusion models.* It is in essence

---

*A more sophisticated approach would include a
rigorous mathematical representation of the causal
relationships determining the waste assimilative and

an economic incentive means for allocating the resource (the waste assimilative capacity of the environment) and can be compared to the peak load
pricing technique used by electrical utilities.[14]

The principal advantage from the economist's
point of view of "internalizing" the cost by means
of a government-levied charge on the source is that
the economic units involved can decide on the best
adjustment to be made in light of the costs and benefits they perceive. Firms that can reduce emissions
at a cost that would be less than the charge will
theoretically do so to avoid being assessed the
charge. Those that cannot reduce emissions at a
cost less than the charge would elect to pay the
fee but would nevertheless have a continuing incentive to reduce emissions. Thus, the optimal level
of pollution abatement will be approached by the
method that is least costly to society as a whole.

Under this system, management rather than government officials would bear much of the burden of
investigation and decision-making. Management, due
to its intimate knowledge of the firm's operations,
is said to be better able to evaluate the advantages and disadvantages of the various ways of dealing with the effluent problem and to choose the best
mix. This is held to be preferable to being restricted to any one abatement technique. Implicit
in the argument of the advocate of effluent fees is
recognition that the optimal level of air pollution
abatement is closely tied to the technological processes involved, with the least-cost solution being
in many cases a complex combination of process
changes and treatment of effluent; in some cases,
moreover, the least-cost solution might involve
partial abatement and payment of the lower effluent
fees associated with the remaining emissions. The
continuing incentive provided by the effluent fee
to search for additional or alternative ways of
abating discharges can involve a different response
than that which might be compelled in a straight
enforcement action. Enforcement by criminal proceeding or by injunction or cease and desist order,
for example, would provide no real alternative to

---

transport characteristics of the ambient air that
would be related to an economic optimization, e.g.,
linear programming model.

incurring the abatement costs, whatever they might
be. Moreover, those enforcement programs that would
require directly or indirectly through pressure the
adoption of specific technology or specific inputs
such as a type of fuel seriously limit the incentive to explore alternative abatement techniques or
to combine approaches to achieve the maximum efficiency in pollution reduction.

A more general advantage of effluent fees is
advanced in William Vickrey's statement that the use
of such fees "forces the administrator to bring the
problem into perspective, and tends to put something
of a restraint on the pure air enthusiast who might
at times be inclined to impose standards that would
entail too high a cost relative to benefits."[15] A
system of effluent fees has additional theoretical
appeal because of its adaptability to changing or
variable circumstances. Fees can be varied up or
down in accordance with weather conditions, the time
of day, the season of the year, and other factors
in order to correlate emitters' costs even more
closely with the damage caused. The theoretical
advantage of this flexibility may be difficult to
realize in practice, however, and indeed may even
prove a liability. Given the great inadequacy of
data and the probabilistic character of the factors
that might be reflected in variable fees, the schedule would take on an appearance of arbitrariness
that might be difficult to dispel. Fee collection
costs would also be considerable.

Other problems with effluent fees are the short-
age of data and lack of agreement on many of the
theoretical problems presented. The major information deficiencies are in the measurement of damages
attributable to particular pollutants and myriad
conceptual and informational problems inherent in
the allocation to individual polluters of the share
of the total damages for which they are "responsible." Perhaps most difficult of all is the theoretical problem of allocating damages to specific polluters when synergistic effects occur--that is,
where the combination of two or more pollutants,
such as sulfur oxides and hydrocarbons, causes
greater damage than either pollutant could cause
alone. Problems of equity are also presented by
the need to allocate damage costs between new and
existing industries. There are also doubts that monitoring technology is adequate to permit effective

enforcement of an effluent fee system. Especially
where there are numerous small polluters to be mon-
itored, such a system would be costly to administer.

Another problem that must be faced in any regulatory system, with or without effluent fees, has
to do with the determination of who should benefit
from the use of the air resource. If air is to be
treated as a free good for the receptors, including
humans, plants, and animals, certain costs are thus
imposed on others who may wish to use the air for
waste disposal. Theoretical discussions seldom deal
with why these costs should not be allocated according to "practical" considerations such as the sup-
posed ability of industrial firms to select and
apply the least-cost solution (including the possibility of paying adjoining landowners to move or
take protective measures). An effluent fee program
might be designed to encourage such flexibility,
but administrative problems would again seem to be
overwhelming in the short run.

A basic complaint against the theoretical under-
pinnings of the effluent fee approach has been raised
by Harold Wolozin, who states:

> My skepticism is based on the unfor-
> tunate fact that we do not know enough
> in an empirical way about the effects
> of taxation on business policies and
> human behavior to be at all certain
> about the outcome of any scheme of
> tax like effluent fees. Even the
> underlying theory can be questioned.[16]

This questioned theory is, of course, the conven-
tional neoclassical microeconomic model, which
depends upon the postulate of rationality and the
concept of the firm as a profit maximizer. He concludes that uncertainty about the effects of taxes
and fees on business decisions militate against the
practicability of a system of effluent fees achieving an optimal level of pollution abatement. Indeed, he envisions a considerable number of negative
surprises that might result in the short run, including misallocation of industry and bizarre price
and cost reactions.[17]

While some of these many problems and data
shortages will handicap any program of enforced

abatement that purports to compare abatement costs
and the benefits derived therefrom, an effluent fee
program would also have to survive legal attacks
based on arguments of apparent discrimination and
abuse of the taxing power. As understanding of the
nature of air pollution and pollution damage costs
increases, effluent fees may become more feasible
and may ultimately fill an important role in air
pollution control. But today, although the assignment or sale of emission or receptor rights has theoretical appeal, the pricing of such rights still
requires some sort of centralized decision-making
system. Such a system, as it might now be constituted in our political and institutional environment,
would yield only a few of the advantages that a
fully market-oriented system, from which it is con-
ceptually derived, would produce. Finally, it is
not entirely clear that this approach would yield
at least a minimum level of air quality at which
negative health effects are avoided.

In sum, effluent fees have solid theoretical
foundations, but the practical problems associated
with establishing and enforcing a fee schedule appear so great that immediate adoption of this approach seems unlikely. Nevertheless, understanding
of the air pollution problem and the regulatory challenge it poses requires a grasp of the effluent
fees' potentiality, since a system of fees may be
the ultimate goal toward which regulation should
evolve.

Payments and Grants

One possible payment system might rely on selective cash grants to waste contributors for the purpose of motivating them to restrict emissions to an
optimal degree. These cash grants would in principle be equivalent to the off-site costs imposed by
increments of waste discharge and would vary with
atmospheric conditions and effluent location, as
well as with the quantity and quality of effluent.
Because this sort of payment would be similar in
theory but opposite in approach to the effluent fee
scheme, the criticisms and difficulties mentioned
above would apply here also.

The more typical proposal under the payments
heading, however, relates to tax relief or subsidies

used in conjunction with direct control. Proposals
for tax relief or subsidies are currently a popular
topic, particularly among industry representatives
and members of Congress,[18] but they have only one
substantial argument in their favor; there is less
resistance to a program of subsidies than to programs of regulation.   There are a number of problems
with the payments approach.   As Edwin Mills states:

> There is a strong practical argument
> against most of the policies under
> the payments heading. They are simply
> payments for the wrong thing. The in-
> vestment credit proposal will illus-
> trate the deficiency that is common to
> others. An investment credit on air
> pollution abatement equipment reduces
> the cost of such equipment. But most
> such equipment is inherently unprofit-
> able in that it adds nothing to reve-
> nues and does not reduce costs. To
> reduce the cost of such an item cannot
> possibly induce a firm to install it.
> The most it can do is to reduce the
> resistance to public pressure for in-
> stallation. Common sense and scattered
> bits of evidence suggest that these
> payments policies are costly and in-
> efficient ways to achieve abatement.[19]

More specifically, it would be difficult to decide
how much to pay to whom for any level of pollution
abatement, for there is no commonly accepted way of
determining an individual polluter's contribution
to ambient air pollution. The taxpayer's feelings
of equity might also be violated because the industrial firm, in not having to consider pollution
abatement a cost of production in the same sense
that labor and capital are, would rely on payments
raised at least partially by higher taxes on other
taxpayers.[20]

Payment schemes, tax credits, or accelerated
depreciation may also bias the technique used for
control in an uneconomical direction because they
tend to promote construction of treatment facilities
when adjustments in production processes, products,
or inputs might achieve the same result at lower
cost and might even increase productivity. Tax

write-offs of capital cost are also at a disadvantage because they are not capable of reducing all abatement costs. It has been estimated that capital cost accounts for only about one eighth of the air pollution abatement costs for a typical firm.[21] Indeed, fuel substitution alone is estimated to be the least-cost alternative in over 60 per cent of the cases involved in air pollution abatement.[22]

Grants and loans have the same objectives as tax write-offs in that they lower the cost of capital expenditures. Thus, the same criticisms apply. However, it has been suggested that if grants were made for both capital and operating costs and administered through regional air quality management organizations, this particular criticism would lose much of its bite.[23] But it suffers from the uncertainties surrounding congressional appropriations. In summary, then, even though the use of payments as an approach to abatement is viable, as experience in England and Czechoslovakia has shown,[24] inherent problems rule it out as a sole means of abatement.

A GENERAL VIEW
OF APPROACHES TO ABATEMENT

Each of these approaches to air pollution abatement has advantages and disadvantages. Thus, the basic question of which approach to abatement is to be used is not of an either-or nature. As Crocker points out, the choice is not between perfect and imperfect systems of control, but between imperfect systems, each with its own set of problems and errors.[25] Until knowledge of control technology and administrative capability can match the demands placed upon them, we will be forced in the short run to live with less than ideal solutions based in part on vague considerations of administrative feasibility and equity. For the near future, the uncertainties involved suggest that broad decision criteria will be more appropriate than highly refined ones.

Thus--even though it has been suggested that the way for dealing with air quality management problems is to use a mix of subsidies, standards, taxes, and

some reliance on market processes[26]--because of the
informational and administrative shortcomings, the
outlook is for programs of direct regulation rather
than the kind of effluent fee approach advocated
by the welfare economist. (As noted earlier, almost all existing programs rely on direct regulation.) Although the data shortages that forestall
the implementation of effluent fees will also plague
programs of direct regulation, the latter approach
is more familiar and can probably sustain a greater
amount of regulation in relative ignorance than
could a more novel system.

But, due to the additional monetary costs associated with the direct regulation approach that
were pointed out above, less than total reliance on
this approach would seem a desirable objective in
reformulating air pollution control efforts. In
advocating a decreased emphasis on direct regulation, Crocker notes:

> If we look upon the control authority
> as being the owner of a donkey with a
> split personality, divided between re-
> ceptors and emitters, we can say that
> the authority will not get the donkey
> to move at an adequate pace by using
> the stick of standards and taxes and/
> or subsidies. Neither will the donkey
> move in the correct manner if the au-
> thority has to stand in front of his
> nose offering him the carrot of mar-
> ket prices. Only if the rider sits
> upon the donkey's back holding the
> stick with the carrot attached to its
> end will the donkey take it upon him-
> self to move correctly. The question
> is the proper length and thickness of
> the stick, and the proper size of the
> carrot.[27]

The Air Quality Act of 1967 requires that states
shall be provided with federally determined air
quality criteria once they are promulgated by the
Department of Health, Education and Welfare, which
is also granted power to review the standards established and the proposed plan of enforcement.[28] As
stated earlier, it is apparently contemplated by
Congress that new state and local legislation would
be forthcoming, and this expectation coupled with a

fairly clear congressional mandate that pollution
control be undertaken in light of technological and
economic feasibility,[29] suggests that new thought
should be given to devising machinery that will
be capable of doing this job more effectively.

It follows that in keeping with the "new federalism," which is often praised as lending itself to
experimentation and innovation in ways of attacking
particular problems,[30] HEW's supervisory powers
could be used to encourage departures from traditional patterns of regulation. Indeed, the regional
approach to regulation specified by the recent act
would seem to anticipate and encourage new departures. Such innovation and experimentation might
produce significantly improved regulatory procedures.[31]

However, before experimental approaches such as
using various mixes of control approaches can be
tried in actual situations it will be necessary to
have some idea of the economic, administrative, and
political problems to which their application in the
short term might lead. It was suggested in the
first part of this study that this can most logi-
cally be done using the rational decision model outlined earlier as a point of departure and integrating experience gained in the study of bargaining.
Although it might be argued that this rational model
is difficult to apply in a complex political and
institutional environment, it does provide a necessary objective toward which one should work and,
possibly more importantly, provides a framework for
evaluating decisions that have been or are going to
be made in air quality management. Thus, the following two case studies, which necessarily deal primarily with direct regulation since this is the only
type of experience available to date, are presented
with a view toward determining ways of bringing
theory and practice somewhat closer together.

THE CASE STUDIES IN PERSPECTIVE

The two case studies of local decision-making
in air quality management cannot really be considered in isolation. Even though the Los Angeles
Air Pollution Control District covers an area in
the Los Angeles Basin that is almost coterminous

with the "problem shed," the role of the state of California and various federal agencies in decisions relating to pollution abatement will shortly become evident. In the case of New York City, since this study concentrates on the on-site incineration issue, little emphasis is given to the fact that a significant amount of the air pollution in the city's air originates in New Jersey and that New York City in turn pollutes the air of that state. Along with these qualifications, some background notes on control efforts in the two urban areas are useful.

The Los Angeles County Air Pollution Control District, a primary example of effective local air pollution control, has been functioning since 1947 pursuant to the California Air Pollution Control District Act noted in Chapter 1. The Los Angeles County Board of Supervisors, sitting as the Air Pollution Control Board, has adopted a broad set of air quality management rules and regulations which have been very successful in abating stationary sources of pollution in the county. Although Los Angeles can boast of much greater practical accomplishments to date in air pollution control than New York City, it is interesting to note that by 1952 both cities had reached the same organizational level. Both had created independent agencies with broad powers to control air pollution--specifically, the power to adopt and enforce rules and regulations[32] and authority to require permits and control devices on pollution-generating equipment.[33] The basis for the California permit system, which can be used as an example, is found in the state enabling act as follows:

> The air pollution control board may require that before the air pollution control officer issues a permit to build, erect, alter, or replace any equipment that the plans and specifications show, and that the permit issued by the air pollution control officer require, that such building, erection, alteration, or replacement will be done in such a manner, and that such approved equipment be used as the air pollution control board finds will eliminate or reduce the discharge of any air contaminants.[34]

The regulation and supervision of equipment by the
issuance of operating certificates has been used
quite extensively in Los Angeles and is a dominant
control technique under current New York City legislation. In fact, the New York City law considerably extended the use of permits by requiring that
much existing fuel-burning equipment and all existing manufacturing processes emitting a sulfur com-
pound obtain operating certificates in compliance
with various time deadlines.[35]

New York City can be contrasted to Los Angeles
in that until 1967 the former has dealt with air
quality within the city government structure without
state enabling legislation. Because the New York
State Legislature was slow in developing detailed
air pollution control measures, the New York City
Council has played a large part in the city's regulatory program. The Council, apparently feeling
that the Board of Air Pollution Control was not act-
ing fast enough in adopting stricter rules, formulated and adopted in 1966 a bill aimed at two major
pollution sources, high sulfur fuels and apartment
house incinerators.[36] In Los Angeles, on the other
hand, almost all regulations have been initially
proposed by the District staff.

The developments covered in the two case studies
occurred over a period starting after World War II
in Los Angeles and during the late 1950's in New
York City. The issues covered are still important
topics of concern in the two areas. The approaches
used to deal with the specific types of air pollution problems covered reflect the political and institutional decision environment at the time and
"the state of the art" in air pollution control
technology. As such, approaches used in the past
will in all likelihood not be entirely applicable
to problem situations that will be faced in the
future. However, the objective of this study is to
point out decision-making strategies that have continuing value together with those that have serious
deficiencies for the long run. With this objective,
the reader should keep in mind the historical development of the political and institutional framework covered in Chapter 1.

NOTES

1. A state-of-the-art review of the technology of air pollution control is found in U.S. Department of Health, Education and Welfare, Air Pollution Engineering Manual, Public Health Service Publication 999-AP-40 (Washington, D.C.: Government Printing Office, 1968).

2. The best example of these procedures is found in Los Angeles. See Los Angeles County Air Pollution Control District, Rules and Regulations, March 3, 1967.

3. A. Kneese, The Economics of Regional Water Quality Management (Baltimore: The Johns Hopkins Press, 1964), 193-95; E. Mills, "Economic Incentives in Air Pollution Control," The Economics of Air Pollution, ed. H. Wolozin (New York: W. W. Norton, 1966), p. 40.

4. For the advantages of direct regulation, see P. Gerhardt, "Some Economic Aspects of Air Pollution" (Paper presented at the Mid-Atlantic States Section, Air Pollution Control Association Conference, October 4, 1967); Waste Management and Control, Pub. No. 1400 (Washington, D.C.: National Academy of Sciences, National Research Council, 1966); U.S. House of Representatives, The Adequacy of Technology for Pollution Abatement, Report of the Research Management Advisory Panel through the Subcommittee on Science, Research, and Development to the Committee on Science and Astronautics, 89th Cong., 2nd Sess., July 1, 1966.

5. For a discussion of federal powers under the statute, see R. Martin and L. Symington, "A Guide to the Air Quality Act of 1967," Journal of Law and Contemporary Problems, XXX (Winter, 1968), 239-74; A. C. Stern, "Implications of the Air Quality Act of 1967," Transactions of the New York Academy of Science, XXX (April, 1968) 759-65. The Public Health Service view is that, although the most accurate measure of pollution would be one reflecting the totality of the effects on health, economics, and aesthetics, information upon which to base such a measurement is not available.

6. The most recent representative statement of this view is U.S. Senate, Air Quality Criteria, A Staff Report of the Subcommittee on Air and Water Pollution, Committee on Public Works, 90th Cong., 2nd Sess., July, 1968.

7. U.S. Senate, A Study of Pollution--Air, Staff Report of the Senate Committee on Public Works, 88th Cong., 1st Sess., September, 1963, p. 20.

8. T. Crocker, "The Structuring of Atmospheric Control Programs," in Wolozin, op. cit., p. 79.

9. P. Gerhardt, op. cit.

10. Ibid.

11. Working Committee on Economic Incentives, Federal Coordinating Committee on the Economic Impact of Pollution Control, Cost Sharing with Industry?, p. 14 (hereinafter cited as "Federal Coordinating Committee").

12. Ibid.

13. A detailed statement of this approach is found in Crocker, op. cit., pp. 61-86.

14. For an explanation of peak load pricing, see P. Steiner, "Peak Loads and Efficient Pricing," Quarterly Journal of Economics, LXXI (November, 1957), 585; J. Hirshleifer, "Peak Loads and Efficient Pricing: Comment," Quarterly Journal of Economics, LXXII (August, 1958), 460; M. Boiteux, "Peakload Pricing," The Journal of Business, XXXIII (April, 1960), 157.

15. W. Virkrey, "Theoretical and Practical Possibilities and Limitations of a Market Mechanism Approach to Air Pollution Control" (Paper presented at the Air Pollution Control Association Conference, Cleveland, Ohio, June, 1967).

16. H. Wolozin, Discussion in Public Health Service, Department of Health, Education and Welfare, Proceedings, National Conference on Air Pollution, December 12-14, 1966, Public Health Service Publication 1649 (Washington, D.C.: Government Printing Office, 1966), p. 580 (hereinafter cited as "Third National Conference Proceedings").

17. Ibid.

18. See U.S. Senate, Air Pollution--1967, Part 3, Hearings before the Subcommittee on Air and Water Pollution of the Committee on Public Works, 90th Cong., 1st Sess., April and May, 1967.

19. E. Mills, "Federal Incentives in Air Pollution Control," in Third National Conference Proceedings, p. 576.

20. E. Mills, "Economic Incentives in Air Pollution Control," H. Wolozin (ed.), The Economics of Air Pollution (New York: W. W. Norton, 1966), p. 45.

21. Federal Coordinating Committee, p. 27.

22. Ibid.

23. Waste Management and Control, op. cit., pp. 225-29.

24. For the British Clean Air Act, see A. R. Smith, Air Pollution (New York: Pergamon Press, 1966). For Czech legislation, see S. Edelman, "Air Pollution Control Legislation," Air Pollution, ed. A. C. Stern (2d ed.; New York: Academic Press, 1968), pp. 581-82.

25. Crocker, op. cit., p. 85.

26. Ibid.

27. Ibid. He goes on to suggest two criteria for judging the proper mix: "The proportion of each element employed must be dependent on the extent to which it can reduce uncertainty and enhance communication."

28. Public Law 90-148, Section 107 (c) (I).

29. Ibid., Section 107 (c).

30. A number of different approaches to control exist on the local level today. See L. Pollack, "Legal Boundaries of Air Pollution Control--State and Local Legislative Purpose and Techniques," Journal of Law and Contemporary Problems, XXX (Spring, 1968), 331-54.

31. The value of this approach is noted in Waste Management and Control, op. cit., pp. 215-21. The experimental approach is in keeping with the American political tradition. D. Price points out that policy decisions have been dealt with on an experimental basis, with the views of interested technical or professional groups having more weight than political or economic theories. D. Price, Science and Government (New York: New York University Press, 1954).

32. New York City Charter and Administrative Code, Ch. 41, Title A, Section 894-2.0 (1963); Air Pollution Control District Act, California Health and Safety Code, Section 24261, (West, 1967).

33. New York City Charter, op. cit., Section 892-3.0; Air Pollution Control District Act, op. cit., Section 24263.

34. Air Pollution Control District Act, op. cit., Section 24264.

35. New York City Charter, op. cit., 892-4.0; Apc Reg. 5.11, 5.17.

36. Local Law 14 (1966).

PART **II**

CASE STUDIES OF LOS ANGELES
AND NEW YORK CITY

CHAPTER **5** THE LOS ANGELES
EXPERIENCE

With the industrial growth and population boom
caused by World War II, Los Angeles also gained an
air pollution problem. The 1,200 square mile Los
Angeles Basin, a mosaic of relatively small municipalities bounded on two sides by mountains, suffers
frequent temperature inversions, light winds, and
a high ozone content in its atmosphere. During the
summer and autumn months, a large high-pressure
area stagnates over the Pacific Ocean off the coast
of California, sending warm air into the Los Angeles
Basin over the top of the ocean-cooled breezes that
skim along the surface. The warm air acts as a lid,
preventing any vertical movement of the cooler air
at the surface. It was thus found in the mid-1940's
that air pollutants originating anywhere in the
basin are carried upward by surface air currents to
the base of the lid or inversion layer where they
accumulate, building up a reservoir of materials
that can produce photochemical smog when acted upon
by sunlight. This layer rises and lowers in response
to changing meteorological conditions.

The first "smog attack" occurred in September,
1943, and such attacks increased in number and in-
tensity during the next few years.[1] It became
readily apparent that this "smog," visible as a
light grey murkiness, restricted visibility and
caused irritation to the eye, nose, and throat. In
response to the worsening problem, Los Angeles officials brought in air pollution experts from eastern
cities who declared that the smog was caused primarily by sulfur dioxide with assistance from smoke
and dust.[2]

Mounting public pressure for the control of air
pollution in Los Angeles resulted in the 1947 passage of the California Air Pollution Control Act,
which authorized the creation of the Los Angeles

81

County Air Pollution Control District (APCD).3 The
District, established by the end of 1947, is gov-
erned by the five Supervisors of Los Angeles County
sitting as the Board of Air Pollution Control, with
jurisdiction over 75 political units and a large
area of unincorporated land. Before the act was
passed, the strongest threat to its viability was
the opposition of the petroleum industry to the
permit system which would require any industry
building a new plant or revising an older plant to
secure a permit to make sure that such plans and
specifications met standards set by the District.
The County Commissioners, by bringing this opposition to the attention of Los Angeles newspapers
and holding a meeting with the major oil companies,
convinced the companies to withdraw their opposi-
tion.4 Initial control efforts were carried out on
a broad front, but first priority was given to
attacking visible sources of pollution--smoke, dust,
and fumes. Much initial effort was given to the
control of refuse burning and major industrial polluters.

EARLY CONTROL EFFORTS

An across-the-board control effort was directed
at industrial dust and fumes from metallurgical
plants, rock-crushing operations, asphalt and paving
processes, the food, paint, fertilizer, and soap
industries, the thousands of orchard heaters used
to prevent frost damage, and diesel trucks and
buses. By the fall of 1948, it was determined by
using air samples that there was a fairly high sulfur dioxide content in the atmosphere; this led to
initial efforts by the District to control such
emissions.5 In response to proposed regulations
aimed at them, the major oil companies said that the
proposed recommendations were "inequitable, too
strict, and would result in unwarranted expense to
the petroleum industry without sufficient proof that
the removal of the sulfur would cure the overall
smog problem."6 Powerful support for the District's
position developed among the public on this issue
and the Los Angeles Times publicly supported the
District.' Thus, the first of a long series of efforts to control the oil industry began.

By 1949, grey iron foundaries were controlled.
The District's hearing board, in response to claims

of excessive control costs, calculated that grey iron costs would be increased less than two mills per pound of product and concluded that this would not be a factor in pricing Los Angeles foundaries out of their competitive market. Within a period of 36 months from the date of the ruling, 36 bag-houses and three electrostatic precipitators had been designed, constructed, and approved by the District.[7] By 1951, the last of the open-hearth steel furnaces in the Los Angeles Basin had installed control devices, and floating lids on oil storage tanks to reduce evaporation of hydrocarbons were universally required.

By the early 1950's, the use of the Ringelmann Chart as a technique for the measurement of smoke emissions had aided in the virtual elimination of the problem of black smoke and soot from the Los Angeles area.* After this removal, it became apparent that there was a serious problem associated with gasoline vapors in that eye irritation and crop damage are caused largely by the oxidation of these vapors to form photochemical smog. These vapors--or hydrocarbons as they are more accurately called-- enter the atmosphere from many sources, such as auto exhausts and losses in the storage, refining, and handling of petroleum products. Thus, the 1954 program of the District called for a major reduction of the emission into the atmosphere of gasoline vapors from automobiles and the control of automo-bile exhausts. (Since this study deals with station-ary sources of pollution, only passing attention is given to automobile air pollution emissions.)[8]

By 1954, six different control approaches had been used in the five preceding years in about 28,000 enforcement actions[9] (a program of zoning to put objectionable industries where they would do the least harm from an air pollution point of view was also given some emphasis). Criminal proceedings, written notices of violations, office hearings,

---

*The Ringelmann chart provides a scale for com-paring the darkness and opaqueness of visible smoke to absolute levels. Published by the U.S. Bureau of Mines, the chart is a series of different line den-sity squares which can be compared to smoke coming from stacks. It was developed in Paris and brought to this country in 1897.

civil injunction actions, Hearing Board actions, and the granting and denial of permits were used. Written notices and cease and desist orders were issued for every violation observed. In more than 90 per cent of the actions that went to the next step of office hearings, compliance was obtained with no further action. In the small minority of cases that went to court, the District chose criminal actions rather than civil actions because of the long time required to complete a civil case. The District's permit system, however, was deemed to be the agency's most effective weapon.[10]

THE INCINERATOR BAN

At the outset of the air pollution control program in 1948, the burning of rubbish was an obvious source of air pollutants; it was estimated that more than 500 tons of air contaminants were released from these sources daily. The first targets for control were the burning refuse dumps. Fifty-five of these were closed by the District, in many cases over bitter opposition and only after court action.[11] From 1948 to 1949, civil action and injunction proceedings were instituted against municipal and private dumps. After 1949, more direct action was employed by taking criminal action against the owners of individual dumps. Following this, all other open fires were restricted. One Los Angeles phenomenon-- the backyard incinerator--and its several thousand commercial and industrial counterparts--proved to be more difficult sources to control. Suggested control measures were met with strong protests from delegations of homeowners and domestic incinerator manufacturers, and it was only when the smog continued to get worse that a control measure was approved.

A number of meetings were held in the early 1950's under the direction of the County Board of Supervisors by the District and the air pollution control committee of the Los Angeles County Division of the League of California Cities in which an attempt was made to find a substitute for the 1.5 million back-yard incinerators.[12] The alternatives suggested were collection by the municipalities or county and (a) county incineration or (b) sanitary landfill. In 1953, the District requested the

the County Counsel for an opinion as to the legality
of a regulation forbidding the disposal of refuse
by burning, except in multiple-chamber incinerators,
or in an incinerator used in conjunction with a
dwelling with not more than four dwelling units.
The County Counsel reported that such a prohibition
would be legal providing it was reasonable from a
practical or engineering point of view. As H.
Kennedy notes, the opinion held that:

> Since the burning of rubbish does
> give off substantial smoke and fumes
> it would be within the jurisdiction
> of the Air Pollution Control Board
> to forbid such burning if it finds
> that the air in the District is so
> polluted as to cause discomfort or
> property damage at intervals to a
> substantial number of inhabitants
> and that the regulation will reduce
> the amount of air contamination in
> the District.[13]

Although the California Air Pollution Control
Act provided that air pollutants could be eliminated
irrespective of their source and it was clear that
the Air Pollution Control District could restrict
these sources of pollution under its police power
by adopting a formal rule at a public hearing before
the Board of Supervisors, the District was still
hard put to justify its decisions due to incomplete
knowledge and inadequate data. Many people thought
that incinerators were an insignificant source of
air pollution that should only be controlled after
industrial emissions were regulated. On the other
hand, the automobile industry was reluctant to reduce the hydrocarbon emissions from cars as long as
pollution from incineration remained untouched. A
variety of "experts" for and against an incinerator
ban were quoted in the newspapers and appeared on
television. As a result, county residents were
sharply divided on the value of the ban.

Partially as a result of a study that showed
that about half of the total charge burned in a
single-chamber incinerator escaped into the air,
the County Board of Supervisors passed the incinerator control measure on June 9, 1955.[14] The first
deadline for ending incineration was October 1,
1955, but, as that date approached, it became obvious

that no other adequate means of refuse disposal
could be provided in such a brief period. To permit the county and communities within the county
to make suitable arrangements, the deadline was
extended to October 1, 1957. However, as the extension was allowed only as a leeway for the
municipalities to arrange service for domestic
users, an advance deadline of July 1, 1957, was
established for stores, factories, and apartment
houses.

The controls on refuse burning instituted by
the District thus occurred in four distinct phases:

(1)   Elimination of municipal and private open
      burning dumps, which was accomplished by
      enforcement action in 1950.

(2)   Elimination of all other types of open
      fire burning related to industrial, commer-
      cial, or residential activities.

(3)   Elimination of industrial, commercial,
      and multifamily waste disposal in single-
      chamber incinerators, accomplished by
      July 1, 1957.

(4)   The ban on all other single-chamber in-
      cinerators, which became effective on
      October 1, 1957.

As a result of these control measures, uncontrolled refuse burning has been effectively prohibited in Los Angeles County since the end of 1957.
Disposal of refuse by burning now is possible only
in multiple-chamber incinerators, with county collection and sanitary landfill the major means
of disposal. Many apartment houses and industries
turned to multiple-chamber incinerators in which
the gases and particulates ordinarily emitted from
single-chamber incinerators are further heated and
burned at temperatures ranging up to 2,000 degrees.
In operation, they proved to emit only 10 per cent
of the pollutants emitted by the ones they replaced.

One of the most significant benefits associated
with these abatement policies was the cessation of
community recriminations traditionally associated
with the Los Angeles smog control effort. Until
the adoption of the ban, it was popular in Los
Angeles County to argue against specific proposed

control measures on the grounds that refuse burning
was an obvious source of uncontrolled air pollution,
and that so long as refuse burning remained uncontrolled, there was no point to controlling other
lesser sources. This view was particularly ascribed
to representatives of the automobile industry, who
often pointed out that auto exhausts probably were
unimportant sources of air pollution compared with
the pollution emissions from refuse burning.[15] The
refuse burning ban ended the relevance of this
argument.

Benefits more susceptible to empirical measurement included a marked decline in public complaints
against specific incinerator operations. Prior to
1957, complaints against such operations led the
list of complaints received by the District. These
complaints decreased 54 per cent from 1957 to 1958.
From 1955 through 1957, three indicators of air
pollution--reduced visibility, plant damage, and
eye irritation--showed a downward trend, and the
number of days during which smog alerts were called
decreased. The fire department also found that,
due to the incinerator ban, the number of individual
responses to alarms was reduced by some 50,000 to
60,000 a year. The cost of removing the refuse
formerly burned has been estimated at about one
dollar per household per month.[16]

THE CONFLICT OVER RULE 62

The mid-1950's was the turning point for the
District. From 1954 through 1956, more than $8 mil-
lion was spent for District operation and research;
the Federal Government was spending only $8.6 million
nationally. By 1957, smog had been reduced to the
level where any significant further reduction would
have to be accomplished by automobile exhaust controls. The most important stationary sources of
air pollutants left in the basin were steam/electric
power generating plants whose burning of fuel oil
to generate electricity yielded large amounts of
sulfur oxides and smaller, but still significant,
contributions of oxides of nitrogen and particulate
matter.

When oil is being burned in such plants, conspicuous plumes are emitted from stacks and particles
that fall in the vicinity often cause property damage.

The solution recognized by the District at this
time was the substitution of natural gas for fuel
oil, which would eliminate sulfur oxides, particulates, plumes, and localized fallout and possibly
reduce oxides of nitrogen by more than half. By
late 1957, the political climate for controlling
sulfur-bearing fuels was favorable because the
District could point to the fact that the households in the Los Angeles Basin had recently absorbed
the costs associated with the back-yard incinerator
ban. The obvious question being asked was: "If
households can absorb these costs, why can't industry?"

The District concluded that large sulfur dioxide concentrations in the atmosphere should be reduced because of a rising tide of scientific opinion
concerning the health effects of sulfur dioxide.
Although there was little basic research, what has
been done suggested to the District staff that sulfur dioxide in the air was a causative factor in
certain illnesses or at least a factor that aggravated certain illnesses.* The critical turning
point for decision was the discovery that the sulfur
dioxide readings in the Long Beach area were as high
as any place in the country and the realization that
much of the sulfur dioxide was being emitted by
public utility power plants.

Because the District realized that the only
clear alternative to burning sulfur-bearing fuel
oil for electricity-generating purposes at that
time was the substitution of natural gas for the
fuel oil,** there was concern for the fact that it
would not be legally possible to force public utilities to change fuels unless there was a guaranteed

---

*Although it was subsequently shown that sulfur
dioxide was a minor agent in the formation of photochemical smog, the primary thrust of later legislation was that sulfur dioxide and sulfates were
dangerous to health in and of themselves.

**Meeting the required limit of anticipated
regulations using fuel oil was not considered feasible since imported crude oil of low sulfur content
would have to be used and such crude oil was under
strict federal control.

source of alternative fuel. Thus, the District
staff as early as 1956 was appearing before the
California Public Utilities Commission in support
of requests for increasing the allocation of natural
gas to Southern California. In mid-1957, the County
Board of Supervisors urged the Federal Power Commission to approve the request of the El Paso
Natural Gas Company to allow the company to construct and operate facilities that would enable El
Paso to carry out exchange agreements for the de-
livery of natural gas to the Los Angeles Basin.
Shortly afterward, the board approved a policy
urging all electricity-generating agencies to take
whatever action necessary to make additional quantities of natural gas available for the use as fuel
in the generation of power. By the middle of
August, 1957, the District initiated a program calling for the voluntary use of natural gas in steam
electric generating plants and large industries
during smog alerts.

By October, 1958, the District was holding
hearings on a proposed rule to require steam power
plants to burn natural gas between May 1 and October
30--the period of minimal demand for natural gas
for space-heating purposes. Although the use of
natural gas was not to be specifically required,
the proposed rule stated that fuel oils containing
more than one half of 1 per cent sulfur were to be
prohibited, together with gaseous fuels containing
more than 50 grains of sulfur per 100 cubic feet
of gas. The only fuel available to meet this requirement was natural gas.

Although the principal impact would be on steam
plants, an estimated 20,000 firms, including manufacturing companies, oil refineries, and ferrous
and nonferrous metal smelting industries would also
be affected. At this time, steam power plants were
using 30,500 barrels of fuel oil a day, refineries
8,000 barrels, and all other industrial sources
16,000 barrels. Whereas the fuel oil used in the
basin at this time had a sulfur content ranging
upward from 1 1/2 per cent, the District estimated
that the measure would eliminate 400 tons of air
contaminants of which more than 272 tons were sulfur dioxide. This would result in an estimated 50
per cent reduction in sulfur dioxide levels in the

air. During this period, "interruptible"* industrial
users of natural gas were using 400 million cubic
feet daily from May through September. Local gas
companies stated they could supply an additional
275 million cubic feet a day, which would be the
equivalent of 48,000 barrels of fuel oil.

When the hearings on the proposed requirement
to burn natural gas were started, public interest
was greater than at any time since the prolonged
debate over the back-yard incinerator ban.[17] The
District took the position that the proposed rule
was needed to prevent a major health catastrophe
and relied on noted consultants to point out
possible developments, such as the lengthy concentrations of sulfur dioxide that had occurred over
Donora, Pennsylvania, and London. The District's
position was that there had been a 100 per cent
increase in sulfur dioxide emissions during the
last seven years and that this rise transformed
the sulfur dioxide problem from mainly a public
nuisance to a potential health hazard even though
a clear cause-and-effect relationship between sulfur dioxide concentrations and illness or death
could not be specified.

The District also argued that to control one
source and not another would be to undermine the
entire pollution control program and would raise
serious doubts as to the equity of other control
measures. Failure to pass the rule was further
viewed as allowing industry to continue to violate
the state health and safety code as well as the
rules of the District. Support for the District's
position came from the Los Angeles County Medical
Association and a citizens group based in Pasadena.

Conflicting testimony came from the former
director of the Air Pollution Control District, who
said that the new rule would do nothing to reduce
air pollution and that the amount of sulfur dioxide
in the air was well below the "allowable" limits

---

*Also referred to as "dump" gas, interruptible
users receive this gas at a reduced rate during
periods when it is not in demand by prime users.
Interruptible customers can have their supply cut
off when prime customers need additional gas.

specified by the state Department of Health. Oil
industry representatives agreed that the rule would
cause "economic disaster" for the local industry in
that $25 million would be lost to the community
without the assured elimination of smog. Western
Oil and Gas Association (WOGA) representatives led
the attack on the District's medical report by
quoting numerous medical and chemistry authorities
who denied that sulfur compounds were proven health
menaces. These spokesmen also argued that the
establishment of a "one fuel" situation would be
dangerous in that natural gas supplies could possibly fail. At the same time, WOGA widely circu-
lated a letter that called for political action to
be taken "directly and indirectly" to block passage
of the rule.[18] This letter led the County Supervisors to charge that the oil industry was guilty
of applying political pressure. The Los Angeles
Chamber of Commerce, although not appearing in
direct opposition to the ban, suggested that evidence be produced that "the penalties fit the crime"
due to the economic impact of the rule on the oil
industry. Small oil producers who were not members
of WOGA also appeared to testify against the ban.

A postponement of 60 days on a Board of Supervisors vote on the rule was proposed by opponents
of the rule so that the data submitted by the District could be checked by "neutral researchers,"
but the plea was denied by board action. The position paper submitted by the District in support of
its proposals emphasized that witness after witness
had held that air pollution is not only a nuisance
but also a possible health hazard and that these
factors cause economic problems whose solution
through pollution control would counterbalance the
economic costs to industry of the oil ban. Aside
from the health issue, the District argued that the
rule was justified even on the basis of the visible
plumes that cause local nuisances and reduced
visibility. When the rule came up for a vote before
the board during the middle of November, 1958, Supervisor Warren Dorn told his fellow supervisors
that if the rule was not adopted a delegation of
District officials going to the 1958 Air Pollution
Control Conference sponsored by the Public Health
Service would be in a very poor position when they
tried to put pressure on the auto industry for a
speed-up on the development of exhaust control

devices. Without the passage of the rule, it was
argued, the auto makers would say that the fuel oil
situation needed to be cleaned up first, just as
they had previously referred to the back-yard incinerators as the source of the problem.[19]

On November 12, 1958, the Board of Supervisors
unanimously passed what became known as Rule 62 and
stated their policy to be "to try to stop air pollution wherever we find it, no matter where it
comes from."[20] In response to the oil industry's
specific contention that the regulation would crip-
ple the local economy, the board left the door open
for later amendments. The law was to go into effect
May 1, 1959.

The first reaction to Rule 62 came in the middle of December, 1958. Dr. Arnold Beckman, who had
been chairman of a blue ribbon committee that had
investigated the nature of smog in 1953, questioned
whether what he termed the "severe dislocations of
the economy" could be justified when only a minor
source of pollution was being attacked.[21] Among
other things, he wanted to know whether:

(1)   a seven month per year ban on fuel oil
      burning would so disrupt the market that
      an adequate fuel oil supply would be un-
      available the balance of the year;

(2)   industrial plants would be forced into a
      one fuel economy without the benefit of
      competitive prices, thus being placed in a
      poor competitive position;

(3)   full consideration had not been given to
      the possible switch from oil to gas when
      weather forecasts predicted the occurence
      of inversions rather than a mandatory seven
      months use of gas.[22]

Dr. Beckman, speaking on behalf of the Chamber of
Commerce, requested that the enforcement of Rule 62
be delayed until all these and other facts were
available. At about the same time, the chairman of
the Federal Power Commission was sounding a warning
at the national Air Pollution Control Conference
in Washington, D.C., that natural gas could not be
counted on as a wholesale replacement for fuel oil.

A month later, the privately financed Air Pollution Foundation filed a report with the Board of
Supervisors which supported the position of the
Chamber of Commerce and the oil companies that sulfur dioxide is not a major contributor to photochemical smog.[23] It also concluded that Rule 62
would not reduce the ozone concentrations in the
atmosphere. About this time (January, 1959), public
opinion polls conducted by local newspapers were
suggesting that the public thought the oil refinery
industry one of the principal sources of air pollution in the Los Angeles Basin.

In January, the oil industry also joined the
public utilities in the voluntary program instituted
in 1957 to switch to natural gas during smog alerts.

In April, 1959, representatives of WOGA urged
the Board of Supervisors to schedule another set
of public hearings on Rule 62 prior to May 1 to
discuss a proposal to "strengthen the rule affecting oil burning by making it year round instead of
for six months."[24] WOGA also wanted all District
research data pertinent to the question made public
prior to the conduct of any such hearings. The
District made the same request of WOGA. On May 1,
1959, Rule 62 went into effect. On May 11, representatives of WOGA formally proposed changes in the
rule. Their position was that the objective of Rule
62 should be to avoid occasional peak concentrations
of sulfur dioxide in the air at times of anticipated
high levels of smog, and that the existing rule imposed an unnecessary burden on industry during the
days when there was no risk of smog. Their proposal
entailed modifying Rule 62 to permit a permanent
fuel switch plan to operate 12 months of the year
in lieu of the complete ban on fuel burning between
May 1 and October 30. The fuel switch would be
mandatory only when the sulfur dioxide concentration
in the air reached one part per million for eight
hours or three parts per million for one hour. It
was noted that the California Department of Public
Health had recently adopted these standards and the
District used them as alert levels. WOGA summarized
its position by saying that its amendments were in
the public interest since existing levels of sulfur
dioxide concentrations in the atmosphere were less
than these standards and the amendments would gear
regulation to accepted health standards and make

them effective on a twelve-month basis rather than just in the summer when oil burning is at its lowest level.

A close inspection of the proposal soon revealed that, if adopted, the amendments would in effect eliminate fuel switching except when heavy smog is forecast. Indeed, in the previous four years the sulfur dioxide levels in the atmosphere set by the Health Department had been exceeded only three times, and these episodes all ocurred within an extremely unusual ten-day period in 1957.[25] The natural gas companies, who had not taken a public position either for or against Rule 62 when it was passed, now opposed the WOGA proposal because they felt they were not able to supply gas on a year round on-again, off-again basis to industry and fulfill their responsibility to eight million firm users without what they considered to be unnecessary price increases. The District re-emphasized that the ban during the summer months was not passed specifically to abate smog concentrations, but because this was the time when the demand for gas for space heating was low, and therefore gas was available for other purposes.

The District staff announced that such a rule change would weaken the whole air pollution control program since the intent of all District regulations was to achieve the maximum possible control of significant sources of air pollution. If the rule were changed, serious questions of law and equity would be raised if such a privilege were extended to one segment of industry but denied to others. The practicability of such a plan was also questioned in that the several thousand fuel oil users who were affected by the rule would have to be notified as to expected weather and would have to have a dual supply of fuel available. The District thought the problems of notification and enforcement would be exceedingly difficult.

In June, 1959, WOGA presented to the Board of Supervisors a panel of experts who testified against the usefulness of the Rule 62 ban.[26] The board took no action on this testimony, and the next activity took place in October, 1959, when the Board of Supervisors received a number of petitions from citizens groups requesting the Rule 62 be extended to the entire year. During this first year, the ban ended

on September 31, which coincided with a heavy smog
episode. Thus, in response to questions at the
December, 1959, meeting of the Board of Supervisors,
a representative of the District stated:

> It is very possible that the rule
> affected visibility in a broad way
> to improve it, but we can't prove
> it. More remotely, it may have had
> an effect on eye irritation, but
> neither experimentally nor observa-
> tionally can we prove it. But
> basically we believe the rule is
> completely justified on the fact
> it prevented visible plumes.[27]

But the District could still document the fact that
the fuel oil ban measurably improved air quality,
stating that estimated emissions of sulfur dioxide
from power plants and refineries were cut from 318
tons to 15 tons per day, while oxides of nitrogen
were reduced by 46 tons per day, and aerosols by
14 tons per day. Visible discharges, or plumes,
from large fuel-burning installations were completely eliminated, and visibility in coastal areas
--the location of most power plants--also showed a
discernible improvement. The District also reported
that recent research findings indicated that sulfur
dioxide possibly acted to speed up the smog reaction
between hydrocarbons and oxides of nitrogen.[28] At
the same time, the District recommended to the
Board of Supervisors that Rule 62 continue in force
as written with its effective period extended as
rapidly as supplies of natural gas became available,
and asked for continued support in the District's
efforts to obtain more natural gas for the Los
Angeles area.

At the same meeting, WOGA challenged the effectiveness of Rule 62 on the grounds that it had
had no effect on eye irritation and visibility, and
stated that, with rare exceptions, sulfur dioxide
concentrations had been far below the State Health
Department's standard when the ban was not operating.
Representatives of local natural gas companies also
warned the Supervisors that the extension of Rule
62 to a year-round basis would result in a more than
50 per cent increase in household natural gas
bills.[29] As the hearing closed, the Supervisors
opposed any further hearings on the ban, stating

that "another public hearing would mean two sets of smog scientists who would testify on opposite sides of this question."

By June, 1960, action was heating up again. WOGA, the California Manufacturers Association, and the Los Angeles Chamber of Commerce sent letters to the Board of Supervisors requesting a change in Rule 62. The Chamber's letter, milder in tone than the other two, asked for a review of Rule 62 but did not advocate particular changes. The WOGA letter re-emphasized its earlier position that (a) there are scores of days during the May-to-October period when the inversion layer is absent and the burning of sulfur-bearing fuels would cause no harm since the pollutants would be readily dispersed; (b) the rule permits unrestricted burning of fuel oil even if sulfur dioxide concentrations are high during six months of the year; and (c) the rule is unreasonable since atmospheric levels of sulfur dioxide in the Los Angeles area are far less than the state standards.[30]

WOGA proposed that what was becoming to be called the "clean fuel rule" be amended so that fuel oil could be burned throughout the year unless one of two specified conditions occurred. First, fuel oil burning would be prohibited when sulfur dioxide levels reached .3 parts per million for at least an hour, with the prohibition ending when levels dropped below this figure. Second, fuel oil burning would be prohibited during any period in which all open burning is prohibited by the provisions of Rule 57. Rule 57, which permits open burning in certain clearly defined situations, such as for clearing agricultural land and for training fire fighters, prohibits such burning on days when the inversion level is lower than 1,500 feet, surface air will not mix any higher than 35,000 feet, and the average wind from 6:00 A.M. to noon is five miles an hour or less. The proposal would also allow the use of combinations of liquid, solid, or gaseous fuels during the prohibition periods, the combustion of which would result in emissions the same or less than the combustion of fuel oil containing 0.5 per cent sulfur by weight.

This proposal, which was probably viewed by the District as a considerable threat to the viability of Rule 62, was met with detailed counter arguments

on August 9, 1960. The District asserted that its
regulations, considered in the aggregate, were
eight times stronger than state health standards,
and that relaxation of the rule would put an in-
tolerable additional burden on the already smog-
laden atmosphere. It was pointed out that the state
standards for ambient air quality set an adverse
level of 1 ppm (part per million) for one hour, or
.3 ppm for eight hours for sulfur dioxide alone.[31]
It seems that, in enacting this standard, the State
Department of Public Health was careful to state
that standards are only guides since, because of
possible synergistic effect due to the presence of
other pollutants, the actual effect of an air contaminant may be felt at lower atmospheric concentrations than those specified by the state standards.

    The state standards, the District noted, also
included levels for photochemical aerosols. Since
no means of measuring these were available, the
adverse level was established through the use of an
"oxidant index." For this purpose, the adverse
level was set at .15 ppm of oxidant for one hour.
Recent work by the District had shown that the presence of minute amounts of sulfur dioxide accelerates
the formation of photochemical aerosols. Therefore,
the District argued that control of sulfur dioxide
should be predicated upon the .15 ppm oxidant level,
and that, since this level was exceeded regularly,
even more stringent control of sulfur dioxide might
be necessary.

    The proposal to impose a ban on fuel oil burn-
ing only when the sulfur dioxide standard or the
specified weather conditions were exceeded drew criticisms because of questions of law and equity that
would be raised if the privilege of emitting contaminants freely during certain periods, but not
during others, were extended to one segment of industry while denied to others. Problems associated
with transmitting legally enforceable instructions
to a large number of fuel oil consumers in a brief
period of time were also raised.

    Relating fuel oil burning to weather conditions
was deemed impractical since, although 70 per cent
of the "Rule 57 days" were predicted accurately,
actual confirmation was only 43 per cent; that is,
only 43 per cent of the forecasts of a Rule 57 day
were actually followed by a Rule 57 day. In other

words, one could expect the forecast requirement of
a shift from oil to gas to prove to be actually un-
warranted--on the basis of the eventual occurrence
of the Rule 57 parameters--57 per cent of the time.
The question of the legality of such a measure was
thus raised. In addition, it was noted that, if
all air pollution regulations were based upon forecasts, it would turn out that such regulations would
be completely relaxed on about three out of every
ten days when weather conditions turned out in fact
to be highly conducive to the accumulation of large
quantities of air contaminants.[32]

The proposal to allow combinations of fuels
to reach the .5 per cent sulfur limit was considered
very difficult to enforce. In order to determine
compliance, it was considered by the District that
almost continuous stack sampling would be required
or extremely accurate metering of the various fuel
flows would be necessary so that the emissions could
be calculated if the sulfur content of the fuels
was known. This would, according to the District,
necessitate all fuel oil users to install expensive
fuel-flow metering equipment or chemical measuring
instruments, which would be a hardship on many, and
it was deemed highly problematical whether sufficiently accurate flow meters existed. In support
of this statement, the District noted that the two
methods of measuring fuel used at electric power
plants--metering daily fuel use and monthly gauging
of tanks--differed by as much as 70,000 barrels of
fuel oil per month.

Stack sampling would require installation of
highly expensive instruments for recording the concentration of sulfur dioxide in the effluent gases,
and flow meters to determine the volume of this
effluent. The District thought that all such equipment would be costly to purchase and maintain and
that the installation of such chemical measuring
devices would probably also require the hiring of
additional personnel skilled in their maintenance
and operation, thereby still further increasing the
cost. The District also thought it entirely possible
that requiring the use of such chemical detection
equipment would be ruled illegal because it might
be considered as forcing a company to testify against
itself. Finally, the District was of the opinion
that under the WOGA proposal they would be just a
"meter-reader" with no discretional authority.

In response to criticisms of a potential one-fuel economy, the District pointed out that hydro-electric power was rising in importance and nuclear power generators were on the horizon. Allegations that there was no evidence that sulfur dioxide caused harm to vegetation were countered with the statement that District investigations had shown that damage to vegetation in the vicinity and down-wind from large installations utilizing fuel oil was extensive, and it was noted that the damage was not done by sulfur dioxide but by a sulfuric acid aerosol that cannot be measured on a continuous air-monitoring basis.

The District agreed that Rule 62 was inadequate in that it applied for only six months of the year but said that it should be extended when more gas became available. Although taking no position on the WOGA proposal, local natural gas companies again said they were opposed to any such "on-again, off-again" industrial gas service.[33] The companies re-emphasized their earlier position that it would be impossible for them to provide gas for large-volume consumers who might want no gas on one day and 100 per cent service on the next. Supporting the gas companies' view, the District noted that the nature of gas supply is such that local gas suppliers must accept gas on the basis of "take or pay" contracts. That is, they agree to accept stated quantities of gas, which they must pay for even if it is not further distributed and consumed. With gas storage limited and costly, it would have been impossible to keep reserve supplies on hand for contingencies. Because, under the proposed amendment, it was probable that 600 million cubic feet of gas per day for power plants alone would be required, the technological and economic problems associated with the proposal were said to be clearly very great.

Finally, the District argued that Rule 62, although not the perfect solution, was the best that could be done under existing fuel supply and technological conditions, and that the basic support for the rule was still Section 24242 of the State Health and Safety Code, which allowed the prohibition of visible plumes.[34] Whereas there was no proof that fuel oil burned alone or in combination with other fuels would not produce such plumes, the District concluded that the WOGA proposal would result in increased violations of state law.

The years of debate on this issue were finally
brought to a head at this time when the Los Angeles
County Counsel declared WOGA's proposed amendment
to be unconstitutional on the grounds that it would
be unfair to other industries and homeowners practicing pollution abatement and would constitute
unreasonable exercise of police powers by putting
smog control on a forecast basis. The opinion
stated that smog forecasts had been so inaccurate
that it would be unreasonable to base a regulation
on such a shaky foundation. The enforcement problem
that would develop if the rules were relaxed against
one group of emitters was also raised, with the
example given of other sources of pollution, such
as household incinerators, claiming equal rights to
exemptions.[35]

This legal opinion was immediately criticized
by the oil industry, not so much because of its
content but because of the manner in which it was
released. WOGA charged that, although their proposal had been in the hands of the County Counsel
for four months, they had had no advance warning of
the sudden release of the opinion on August 8, 1960.

No further activity took place on the Rule 62
ban until February and March of 1961. At this time,
WOGA again raised the same points it had emphasized
for the previous years; namely, that sulfur dioxide
is not dangerous to health, does not increase eye
irritation, does not reduce visibility, and does
not damage vegetation. WOGA also presented an economist who argued that the rule was pushing the price
of natural gas so high that local industrial firms
would not be able to compete with those located
elsewhere. WOGA argued that to continue to supply
natural gas to industrial users on a noninterruptible
basis would require the expansion of gas transmission facilities at a cost that would affect domestic
prices and that new gas contracts would have the
same effect. It was also asserted that the use of
fuel oil only during part of the year raised prices
during the rest of the year due to a withdrawal
of fuel oil from the Los Angeles market.

The weeks preceding this testimony had seen a
public relations campaign by the oil interests de-
picting Rule 62 as a hardship on the Los Angeles
economy. Almost without exception, the Metropolitan
newspapers had also editorialized that the rule was

an economic burden, and the Los Angeles County
Chamber of Commerce, the Los Angeles Department
of Water and Power, as well as distinguished community leaders supported this position. At the
same time, groups interested in keeping the rule
in effect--such as the Stamp Out Smog organization--
picketed outside the offices of the Board of County
Supervisors.

During this last debate on Rule 62, the crux
of the issue was increasingly the economics of
the oil industry versus public health. Spokesmen
for the Los Angeles County Medical Association and
the U.S. Public Health Service said that air pollution had reached a point in Los Angeles where no
relaxation of rules was safe. Medical men speaking for WOGA argued that harmful effects from the
then current level of fuel oil burning had not been
established. This point was not directly refuted,
with the position taken by the District in effect
expressed by a representative of the Public Health
Service: "We can't wait for legal proof for what
damage air pollutants are doing to human tissues.
We must act now to clean the air."[36]

The District presented evidence that Rule 62
decreased oxides of nitrogen emissions from power
plants by 53 per cent, an amount said to be equal
to the combined oxides of nitrogen output from approximately one million motor vehicles. It was
emphasized that this was one of the primary smog-
causing agents and had reached an alert level in
Los Angeles for the first time four months earlier
with a subsequent occurrence a month later. County
Counsel again emphasized that the entire control
program would be jeopardized if the rule was changed,
because others restricted by control regulations
would be entitled to equal treatment under the law.

The charge that costs of natural gas and fuel
oil were going up was countered with the assertion
that, even if there was a price increase due to
the tapping of a new gas field, the domestic charge
increase would be only six cents per month and that
fuel oil could be made available to meet the Los
Angeles non-Rule 62 wintertime demands through increased use of storage facilities.[37] At the worst,
this was said to raise the price of fuel oil $0.63
per barrel to a level of $2.67, which was said to
be well below 1957 posted ($2.80) and actual ($3.06)

prices. The District concluded that the total economic burden of Rule 62 would therefore be about
one-third the cost of the incinerator ban, in return
for a far greater reduction in contaminant emissions.

On March 16, 1961, after hearing nine hours of
testimony, the Board of Supervisors unanimously
voted to deny the petition of WOGA for a relaxation
of Rule 62 and instead voted to extend the coverage
of the rule an additional thirty days to a seven-
month period from April 15 to November 15 of each
year. By the time of the vote, the board had heard
more than 35 hours of testimony in ten different
hearings. The final decision was precipitated, it
seems, by the warning of the District's experts
that the WOGA proposal would result in a public
health hazard with potential catastrophic proportions and that smog was forcing people to leave the
Los Angeles Basin. The ban was extended the additional thirty days because additional supplies of
natural gas had become available.

At this point, the issue faded from public view,
but it was by no means settled. WOGA brought a
legal suit in the Superior Court, and very extensive
briefs were filed on both sides. Although a County
Counsel's brief is usually about 25 pages, in this
case, it was approximately 380 pages. A hearing
was not set immediately, and it turned out that the
case was not heard in its entirety for almost five
years! Indeed, it was not until early 1964 that the
lawsuit again received public attention. The re-
newed activity was based in part on a serious concern by the oil interests that they were losing an
additional share of the fuel market in the Los
Angeles Basin. This concern was justified in that
in January, 1964, the County Board of Supervisors,
on the recommendation of the Air Pollution Control
District, had enacted Rule 62.1, which had the effect of compelling industrial fuel users and public
utilities to burn only natural gas whenever it is
available during the November 15 to April 15 period
of each year. This rule was passed when it became
apparent that substantial quantities of natural gas
available for use during the non-Rule 62 period
were not being used. The gas was turned back at
the state border by the gas companies because the
larger users such as the power plants of the Edison
Company and the Los Angeles City Department of Water
and Power were committed to burn large supplies of

oil for which they had already contracted to assure
themselves a supply of fuel oil adequate to last
them through a cold winter. The power plants thus
found it advisable to contract with their oil sup-
plier to take or pay for a minimum of many million
barrels of oil, thereby being in a position of having to burn oil even when gas was available. Rule
62.1 ended this procedure.

The suit contended that the District's rulings
were (a) doing nothing to correct smog conditions,
(b) injurious to the area's economy, and (c) illegal. The last point contended that the state legislature created the District only to regulate
emission of noxious fumes, and the District was exceeding its authority by prohibiting use of specific
fuels. The first two points were basically reiter-
ations of the arguments raised before the Board of
Supervisors and also a repeat of arguments being
raised at the same time before the Federal Power
Commission in Washington, D.C.

The suit finally went to trial in August, 1965.
Initially, the WOGA attorney was careful not to attack the District directly, possibly for public
relations reasons, but on about the eighteenth day
of the trial, the judge raised the question of
whether the District's power to make rules having
penal sanctions was an unconstitutional delegation
of legislative authority. Thus, the case was decided in Superior Court almost entirely on constitutional grounds, and the county prevailed on its
point that it had not exceeded its authority in
banning the use of fuel oil containing more than
0.5 per cent sulfur whenever natural gas was available.[38] WOGA entered a motion for a mistrial,
arguing that it was impossible to get a fair trial
in Los Angeles County due to the "atmosphere of
hysteria" induced by publicity concerning potential
damage to health from smog. The request for a transfer of the trial to another location was denied.
WOGA then appealed this 1966 decision but eventually
withdrew this appeal in early 1968. Why this appeal
was withdrawn is still open to conjecture, but it
can probably be related to other developments in
the Los Angeles Basin and in Washington, D.C. Possibly the oil companies were by this time making
sufficient money selling low-sulfur fuel within the
basin so that Rule 62 no longer seemed undesirable
but actually had enhanced the market.[39] Another

line of reasoning suggests that the suit was part
of a larger strategy to affect the outcome of a
Federal Power Commission case on the importation of
natural gas into Los Angeles, and that developments
in that case caused the oil industry to change its
position. The lawsuit, however, had by the time
of its hearing assumed secondary importance because
of the prominence given to efforts to find additional natural gas to burn in the steam electric
generating plants in the basin.

THE IMPORTATION OF NATURAL GAS

From 1956 on, the District had been continually
seeking an increased allocation of natural gas for
Southern California from the California Public Utilities Commission and the Federal Power Commission.
Whereas the history of these efforts from 1956 to
the present is voluminous, only certain aspects of
this issue of direct interest are emphasized here.
In essence, the objective of the Air Pollution Control District was to substitute natural gas for fuel
oil for as much of the year as possible, and by mid-
1961 the District was on record as favoring the use
of gas for the whole year. The District was thus
actively engaged in attempting to influence decisions made at a considerable distance outside Los
Angeles. The nature of these decisions are best
explained by briefly reviewing the history of the
use of natural gas in Los Angeles and noting the
positions of the various participants in this history.

The first out-of-state supply of natural gas
arrived in Los Angeles in 1947 through a pipeline
of the El Paso Natural Gas Company.[40] Later, El
Paso added a second line and boosted its supply until it furnished 70 per cent of the gas used in the
region. A second company, Transwestern Pipeline
Company, entered the market in 1960, and, as of
1961, the two companies were supplying 80 per cent
of the gas used. The remainder came from California
sources. The market for gas was growing rapidly
because of Rule 62 and increased domestic consump-
tion. The market for electricity was also growing,
and Southern California Edison, a public utility
supplying nearly half of the customers in Southern
California, was finding itself using more and more
natural gas to generate electricity.[41] This was

because gas on an interruptible basis was cheaper
than fuel oil and was preferred by the Air Pollution
Control District. In 1960, about 40 per cent of
the gas sold by the gas companies within California
went to industrial and utility customers such as
Edison on an interruptible basis. Edison was the
largest single customer, with 10 per cent. As noted
earlier, these industries would use fuel oil when
the firm gas customers--homes and stores--increased
their demand. This procedure permitted the gas
companies to meet peak demands in winter for home
heating while still having a large market in the
summer for their gas, thereby keeping the price
down, particularly for the interruptible customer
who received the lowest rate--only one third of the
firm rate paid by residential users.

     With increasing pressure from the Air Pollution
Control District to burn more natural gas, and with
an eye on the rising price of gas--up 80 per cent
in ten years--Edison, which was later joined by the
Los Angeles City Department of Water and Power,
sought to obtain a firm supply of gas at a predic-
table price. Although Edison realized that a firm
supply would be somewhat more expensive, the company
believed that it was the only way to ensure an adequate supply. Their plan was to use a new out-of-
state pipeline to be constructed by the Tennessee
Gas Transmission Company (now known as Tenneco,
Inc.) which did not have an outlet in Southern
California. Naturally enough, the local gas companies charged that a new importation of gas would
disrupt the balance in the market and they would
have to work out more expensive ways of meeting
peak demands for home heating in winter if the interruptible outlet was no longer available during
the summer. The local companies were Pacific Lighting and its subsidiaries, Southern California Gas
Company and Southern Counties Gas Company, which
had complete control over all imported gas as well
as most of the locally produced gas. (The pipelines
feeding the region stopped at the state border,
where Pacific Lighting picked up the fuel in its
own lines.) They did not relish another competitor
in the field, nor did El Paso and Transwestern.
The oil interests, of course, also opposed the Edison plan.

     While Edison and the local gas companies carried
on formal negotiations for a long period of time in
an attempt to provide Edison with firmer supplies,

neither party was very precise on why a firm agreement did not emerge. In any event, Edison secretly signed a contract with Tennessee Gas Transmission Company while negotiations were still going on. This was in December, 1957. During this and later periods, Edison repeatedly insisted it would not be looking for a large gas supply were it not for the pressure of the Air Pollution Control District and public opinion calling for less use of fuel oil and more use of gas to reduce air pollution.

Decisions on the issue of increased use of natural gas could not be made directly by the District. The California Public Utilities Commission (PUC) and the Federal Power Commission (FPC), which held the responsibility for determining the public interest in the allocation of a constrained supply of natural gas, would make the final decision. Decisions on the use of natural gas to control air pollution were without precedent; the Federal Power Commission had never approved a gas line designed to provide boiler fuel for steam generating plants exclusively. Efficiency questions were also being raised, for the use of natural gas to generate electricity is admittedly inefficient, for part of the electricity is used to heat stoves and water tanks, a function gas can perform directly. Thus, hearings on the issue produced mountains of data and testimony. As of January, 1962, more than 150 attorneys representing 53 law firms from coast to coast had participated in hearings on the issue, 42 witnesses had offered direct testimony, and transcripts totaling 6,611 pages, with an estimated aggregate of 1,718,860 words, had been compiled.[42] By this time, it had become clear that the recognition of a connection between air pollution and public health would ultimately prove to be the critical issue in the commission's decisions.[43] The big problem for the Air Pollution Control District, then, was to get the PUC and FPC to consider the allocation of natural gas on the basis of public health arguments in addition to economic and conservation considerations.

The District's approach was to act as an intervener in hearings before the FPC in behalf of the applicants--Southern California Edison and the Department of Water and Power. Over the period of a decade, the arguments it presented emphasized the same basic points. These were that the burning of natural gas would reduce the health dangers of

sulfur dioxide in the atmosphere and that the
additional cost of the use of this fuel was not
excessive. The FPC commissioners were notably unre-
sponsive to these arguments. Thus, the first major
proposal, that of the Tennessee Gas Transmission
Company, was withdrawn after the hearing examiner
argued that existing lines should be filled to capacity before any new lines were authorized. The
FPC's view of the evidence and testimony presented
by the District has been summarized as follows:

> (1)   The data submitted relating to
> health aspects "contains a prolifer-
> ation of unoffered, unadmitted, in-
> admissible, and often irrelevant,
> hearsay material."
>
> (2)   To the extent that gas is needed
> in Los Angeles, it has always been
> available.
>
> (3)   Substitution of natural gas for
> fuel oil cannot be said to be in the
> public interest if the cost to the
> community is totally disregarded.
>
> (4)   Burning of fuel oil contributes
> only negligible quantities of carbon
> monoxide and hydrocarbons, which are
> the two greatest polluters of the Los
> Angeles atmosphere; oxides of nitro-
> gen levels cannot be correlated with
> fuel oil burning; and high concentra-
> tions of oxides of nitrogen are not
> attributable to fuel oil burning.
>
> (5)   Los Angeles has the lowest sul-
> fur dioxide concentration on the aver-
> age of any major city.
>
> (6)   An Air Pollution Control District
> publicity release states that when
> automobile emissions are brought under
> control smog will no longer be a prob-
> lem in Los Angeles. Thus, it would
> be illogical to spend any effort to
> control fuel oil, which has a toler-
> able level of emission of pollutants,
> where the total pollution from the
> large source will be reduced in the
> near future.

> (7)   It was noted that "it is partic-
> ularly significant to note that the
> medical testimony quoted does not dis-
> cuss any relationship between health
> and stack emissions."44

It is obvious that the FPC staff was not overly
impressed with the same arguments that the District
presented to the County Board of Supervisors. Holding that gas has its highest and most efficient use
in residential heating, the staff severely questioned
the use of gas for boiler fuel without a proven need
for such use. In like manner, a similar proposal
advanced in 1962 by El Paso Natural Gas and the
Colorado Interstate Gas Company was rejected by an
examiner, the reasoning being advanced that there
were sufficient supplies of gas available through
existing lines for years to come. The next proposal
that was eventually turned down, that of the Gulf
Pacific Pipeline Company, a subsidiary of the Tennessee Gas Transmission Company, can be documented
in some detail to show the factors involved in all
of the FPC decisions.

In March, 1963, the Los Angeles Department of
Water and Power signed a 20-year supply contract
with Gulf Pacific, thereby rejecting a bid from the
Pacific Lighting companies to continue to supply
their gas on an interruptible basis. The advantages of the Gulf bid, as listed in a trade journal
at the time, were:

> (1)   It offered a dependable, uninter-
> ruptible gas supply over the 20-year
> contract period.
>
> (2)   The cost of the Gulf Pacific gas
> would be relatively stable whereas the
> local gas companies' bid prices could
> be increased at any time by the Cali-
> fornia Utilities Commission.
>
> (3)   Gulf Pacific obligated itself to
> deliver from 80 per cent to 90 per
> cent of the total annual quantities
> required by the Department of Water
> and Power, whereas the two local com-
> panies limited their obligations to
> 70 per cent.

(4) The local gas companies' supply
would be subject to interruption during the five winter months not now
covered by Rule 62.[45]

Shortly afterward, Southern California Edison
joined the Department of Water and Power in the
agreement, resulting in a contracted supply of nearly
five trillion cubic feet worth an estimated $1.5
billion over the life of the contract. A contract
of this magnitude was sure to be hotly contested
before the FPC.* In this case, the fight was essentially between Transwestern and El Paso Gas on
one hand, whose interests coincided because of their
existing hold on the gas transmission market, and
Gulf Pacific, which wanted to bring in a new pipeline to serve the two utilities. The basic contention of Gulf Pacific was that additional natural
gas would help alleviate the smog problem caused
by the burning of oil to heat the boilers in the
steam generating plants. Interveners on the side
of Gulf Pacific were the Air Pollution Control District, Edison, the Department of Water and Power,
and the County Counsel. WOGA and the local gas
companies intervened on the opposite side. Both
parties presented essentially the same points that
were argued in hearings on the passage of Rule 62
and the subsequent lawsuit, although by this time
additional research and data-gathering made the
testimony much more voluminous than the original
1958 Rule 62 hearings. Between June, 1964, and
March, 1965, 28,000 pages of testimony were presented.[46]

The District relied on various medical specialists to present its health hazard argument.
WOGA characterized this testimony as "assorted myths
and legends" and labeled the witnesses of the District, the U.S. Public Health Service, and the California Department of Health as "dreamers carrying
placards saying: Today is the end of the World."[47]

------

*Federal law permits direct sale of natural gas
in interstate commerce outside of regulatory channels, but any pipeline required to move this gas is
under the regulation of the FPC. Thus, the FPC
would rule not on the sale of the gas but on its
movement.

County Counsel attacked the contention of the local
gas companies that the supplying of natural gas to
power plants year round would increase the cost of
gas to householders, stating that the Pacific Lighting companies' own figures showed that 100 per cent
service to the power plants would not increase the
cost to domestic users, but even if there were an
increase in gas prices, the cost would not be unreasonable in relation to expenditures already made
in Los Angeles for air pollution control.

He also attacked testimony by Pacific Lighting
contending that smog occurs only on warm days, when
there is enough gas to supply power plants. Evidence introduced in rebuttal by the District showed
that smog manifestations occur throughout the year
regardless of temperatures, that concentrations of
primary pollutants are higher in the winter, and
that damage from power plant emissions occurs only
when oil is burned. Mention was also made of the
fact that visible plumes violate state and county
laws. Finally, the District argued that the desirability of substituting natural gas for fuel oil
had already been decided by the responsible authority, the County Board of Supervisors, and that it
would be improper for a federal regulatory body to
frustrate local policy.[48]

As the lengthy hearings progressed, the testimony of the Air Pollution Control District seemed
to have made an impact. In June, 1965, the California Public Utilities Commission took the side of
the Gulf Pacific Company, which meant that the Commission would support the Gulf Pacific proposal before the FPC. A more significant event occurred
in December, 1965, when an FPC examiner approved
the Gulf Pacific proposal, asserting that Pacific
Lighting had failed to meet its responsibility to
Southern California Edison and the Department of
Water and Power by not responding to public demands
that only gas be burned in the Los Angeles Basin
generating plants. The examiner stated that additional gas was needed because of "insistent demands
of public opinion made indignant by an increasing
air pollution problem" which had "created public
pressures on the electric companies to burn gas in
their generating plants."[49] He also argued that,
although advances had been made in reducing sulfur
emissions during fuel oil combustion, the emissions
were still unsatisfactory and that "the most

promising technical and physical means of reducing
air contaminants from steam electric generating sta-
tions is to substitute natural gas for fuel oil."[50]
His two other points were that (a) the public utilities face regulatory bans against burning fuel
oil, and (b) medical testimony asserts that air pollution is harmful.

Unfortunately for the Air Pollution Control District, the examiner's approval had to go before the
full Commission for review. In January, 1966, the
examiner's recommendation was rebutted in a brief
filed by the Commission's legal staff assigned to
the case. The brief argued, in effect, that air
pollution was a secondary issue and that there was
no relationship between the sulfur dioxide emissions
from power plants and negative health effects. At
this point, the Department of Health, Education and
Welfare offered the testimony that the health factor was an important one in the Los Angeles situation and also argued that every large metropolitan
area that had an air pollution problem and wanted
more natural gas should be allowed to get it. The
Commission's legal staff prevailed, however, and
the Commissioners voted four to one to overturn the
examiner's recommendation. The main aspects of the
opinion, issued in July, 1966, are as follows:

> (1) The record fails to demonstrate
> that the introduction into Los Angeles
> market of enough gas to eliminate com-
> pletely the burning of fuel oil during
> winter months would have appreciable
> effect upon the smog problem or any
> beneficial effect on health of people.

> (2) On the basis of the particular
> situation in Los Angeles, the evi-
> dence in record and the current state
> of technology and scientific under-
> standing of air pollutants and their
> effect on human beings, the Commission
> concludes that none of the proposals
> here would have any appreciable ef-
> fect upon the health of people of Los
> Angeles.

> (3) Absent unusual circumstances
> there is no reason to certificate
> duplicative service to particular

industrial customers where the local
distributor indicates a willingness
and ability to serve.

(4)   The certification of the Gulf
Pacific proposal under the rate structure proposed here would have substantial adverse impact on the public
interest.

(5)   Technology with respect to
treating power plant emissions to reduce pollutants is in a state of
change; Gulf Pacific with its fixed
supply and customers under 20-year
contract is peculiarly ill-adapted to
meet the situation.

(6)   The prospect of committing two
electric companies to using natural
gas exclusively to generate power until 1988 is not an attractive alternative to the inherently flexible TSP
(Tailored Supply Program of the local
gas companies), either from an economic or air pollution standpoint.

(7)   One of the most compelling reasons for certificating TSP is that it
leaves the Federal Power Commission
and the California Commission in a position to take whatever action future
circumstances may require.

(8)   The TSP proposal is clearly preferred to the Gulf Pacific proposal
because it (a) more clearly meets peak
day and annual market needs; (b) is
substantially cheaper; (c) avoids serious problems of high field prices upon
which the Gulf Pacific proposal is predicated; and (d) provides for necessary
flexibility in the use of gas in the
Los Angeles market over the next two
decades of rapid change.

(9)   There is no validity to the argument that the determination of the necessity of providing natural gas to a
community to combat air pollution is
solely for local authorities.[51]

The Commissioners clearly wanted to maintain flexibility in the use of natural gas, thereby allowing for (a) future competition from nuclear energy and distant coal burning for the generation of electricity and (b) technological change that would result in the use of catalytic converters and other equipment to remove sulfur dioxide from flue gases. But, in the final analysis, the major force behind the Commissioner's decision was the belief that the allocation of natural gas to Los Angeles for air pollution abatement would most likely set a precedent for other cities with sulfur dioxide problems.[52] Indeed, at the time of the decision, New York City also had an application for additional natural gas on file.

In favoring the El Paso and Transwestern application, the FPC was still sanctioning an additional flow of natural gas to Los Angeles, but at a lower level. Thus, the favored proposal would supply 590 million cubic feet as opposed to Gulf Pacific's 865 million cubic feet. The 590 million cubic feet would provide a ten-month supply versus the seven-month supply then available--a gain of three months' supply. The 590 million cubic feet was assured at least through 1968 but would be on an interruptible basis.

A month after the Commissioners' decision, Southern California Edison petitioned for a rehearing, charging that the FPC based its conclusions as to critical cost issues on off-the-record studies that showed inconsistencies and glaring errors and that Edison was never given the opportunity to cross-examine compilers of the studies. The petition was denied, and attention shortly shifted to a new solution to the problem of sulfur dioxide emissions.

THE IMPORTATION OF LOW-SULFUR OIL

By May, 1967, Southern California Edison representatives were back in Washington, D.C., but this time at the Department of the Interior with a request for permission to import ten million barrels of Indonesian oil for the coming winter. It seems that shortly before this Standard Oil of California and Texaco had come forward with a low-sulfur, low-ash fuel that could meet the requirements of Rule 62.

Supplied from Indonesian oil fields, the sulfur content was only 0.2 per cent compared with the 2 per
cent in fuel oil then being used. The Secretary
of the Interior, under executive order from the
President to strongly support environmental quality
programs, was more taken with the air pollution
arguments than the FPC had been and, in July, 1967,
announced a modification of the oil import program
to encourage the use of low-sulfur fuel oil.[53] The
modification came through broadening of the definition of residual fuel oil. It was changed to include No. 4 fuel oil, which has properties similar
to ordinary high-sulfur residual oil but generally
with less sulfur. Heretofore, No. 4 fuel oil had
been defined as a finished oil product, subject to
rigid import quotas. The new definition also included low-sulfur crude oils that may be burned directly as fuel oil with no processing.

By October, 1967, representatives of the Air
Pollution Control District were also back in Washington, in this instance testifying against a bill
introduced in the Senate that would take away from
the Secretary of the Interior the authority to set
oil import quotas and place them completely under
the control of Congress. It would also have prohibited the consideration of air pollution as a
factor in the regulation of oil imports. This bill
was not passed, but the District views such legislation as a continuing threat because of repeated
efforts by protectionist-oriented Congressmen from
oil-producing districts to reduce oil importation
from abroad.[54]

The latest development has been the surprise
availability of low-sulfur fuel from Alaska. At
the present time, it seems that the Alaskan fields
will have the potential of supplying much of the
needs of the Los Angeles Basin for fuel oil during
the two months of the year when natural gas is not
available.[55]

THE LOS ANGELES EXPERIENCE REVIEWED

In its 20-year history, the Los Angeles Air Pollution Control District has gained a reputation for
combining militance and political adroitness in a
very successful air pollution control effort. Since

its establishment, the District has adopted more
than 100 rules and regulations governing the emissions of air contaminants from stationary sources.
These rules and regulations govern smoke, nuisance,
particulate matter, sulfur compounds, combustion
contaminants, dust and fumes, open fires, incinerator burning, storage of petroleum products, oil
effluent-water separators, gasoline loading, sulfur
content of fuels, gasoline composition, solvents,
and animal reduction processes. These rules have
been rigidly enforced, with a 97 per cent conviction
rate of the more than 35,000 violators taken to
court.

This abatement effort has been concurrent with
the major effort to control the emissions of automobiles. From 1940 to 1960, the number of cars in
the Los Angeles Basin increased from one million to
three million, a rate of increase expected to continue in the future. Although Los Angeles has been
the acknowledged leader in initiating control measures on automobile emissions, such emissions now
account for a large percentage of the air pollution
in the Los Angeles Basin. Because of the ubiquitous
nature of the automobile, state and federal legislation have superseded the District's early control efforts in the sense that emission control
devices are now required by the state and Federal
Government.[56] Thus, even though the automobile emissions characterize the Los Angeles type of smog,
the real indicator of the success of the Los Angeles
County Air Pollution Control District is the control
of stationary sources of pollution.

The Control Agency's Approach
to Abatement

Prior to 1940, as far as is known, air pollution levels in the atmosphere in the Los Angeles
Basin had not passed the threshold at which they
had become conspicuous. Therefore, the District
has in the past looked upon the level of pollution
in the atmosphere existing before that date as the
goal of their control efforts. But because no measurements of air quality were being made in those
days, the specification of this objective could
only be estimated. Because of the perceived seriousness of the air pollution problem in the Los
Angeles Basin, the Board of County Commissioners

has continued to give the District over the years a mandate: Get rid of air pollution. Thus, the District has operationalized its stated goal in the form of a "first and foremost principle" that all industrial, domestic, and vehicular operations should be carried out with essentially no emissions to the atmosphere. (In response to a request for a characterization of the stringency of the District's standards insofar as industrial pollution is concerned, County Supervisor Warren Dorn replied, "We just don't allow it.")[57]

The District's position is that during the time that the District has operated, Los Angeles has continued to have a severe air pollution problem and that the public has very clearly expressed its will that air pollution be eliminated. The District sees its function as the completion of this task as rapidly as possible. Due to the perceived severity of the problem, the opinion is that only now is the District approaching a position where it can "afford the luxury" of discriminating between different kinds of pollutants. Due to insufficient information, decisions have necessarily been made on the basis of judgment rather than from a position of complete understanding. As public officials, members of the District take the position that it is not possible for them to wait ten years for a study that will specify an A-to-B relationship when it is suspected that existing levels of air pollution have harmful effects.

Thus, the District does not feel the need to specify an exact relationship between air pollution and health, arguing that if success is achieved in reducing smog, the health situation would without doubt be improved.* The District's unsuccessful attempt before the FPC to specify such a cause-and-effect relationship probably reinforced this view.**

----

*The District has found that an argument for air pollution control based on aesthetic considerations is not considered in litigation proceedings to be pertinent. Assistant Director Robert Barsky, however, believes that the police power is perfectly designed to protect aesthetics even though few cases have been decided on it.

**As noted earlier, the FPC's decision was probably not based as much on the health arguments as

Thus, in the District's presentation before the Secretary of the Interior on low-sulfur oil imports, the argument was related to gross manifestations-- the visible plume, the visible fallout, the visible damage to property, and the "common-sense" relationship between these factors and the interference with the enjoyment of life and the general implications for health.* This view has also resulted in the policy of attacking photochemical smog, nitrous oxides, and sulfur dioxide by using available technology to control the visible plume, dust, and fumes, after emphasizing the visible effects such as damage to property and the fact that these emissions add to over-all levels of emissions.

It appears that the agency has adopted the general position that, because the close relation between health and air pollution is difficult to prove, its rationale for control should be that a nuisance interferes with comfortable living as a basic right and that there is no basic right to use the air as a sewer. Thus, the very important permit system used by the District is based on the "reservoir concept," which requires that the applicant demonstrate that he will not impinge on the basic rights of others by polluting the air.

The Permit System

The District believes that the permit system has proved to be a very effective means of controlling air pollution. Underlying the use of this system in Los Angeles is the concept that no one has a right to pollute the air, but rather that society has a paramount right that the air remain clean. Thus, if an individual proposes to conduct activities likely to create air pollution, he must first obtain a permit which is granted only after it is established that required safeguards are present.

---

on the fact that they did not want to establish the precedent at that time of providing natural gas for boiler fuel exclusively.

*Due in part to the executive order from the President, as noted earlier, the Secretary of the Interior was also more open to environmental quality considerations than he was earlier.

The effectiveness of the District's permit system rests on a two-step method of issuing permits. The first step requires the applicant to obtain an "authority to construct" before any equipment capable of emitting or controlling air contaminants is constructed, altered, or replaced. If the applicant's plans and specifications show that the equipment can operate within prescribed limits, an authority to construct is granted. If the equipment is deemed capable of emitting air contaminants that will create a public nuisance, or of violating any of the sections of the State Health and Safety Code or the District's rules and regulations, then permission to construct, alter, or replace such equipment is denied. Granting an authority to construct, however, does not constitute a "permit to operate." The second step requires that the applicant actually operate the equipment within the prescribed limits in the presence of an air pollution engineer, with approval of such source tests based on equipment performance. Only then is a "permit to operate" granted. This permit remains in effect only as long as its conditions are observed. The District charges a fee for these permits. The concept underlying the fee charge is that those requiring special service from the District should pay the major share of the cost of providing it.

Weighing the Benefits and Costs

The District staff views itself as being composed of "highly qualified scientists and engineers," but staff members emphasize that they make no pretense at being economists. Although some balancing of benefits and costs is done by the staff, benefit-cost analysis is viewed as a gambit to avoid and delay.[58] As such, they think of it as a strategic tool used by polluters to advance their case against control. But within the agency, benefit-cost analysis has been used in very generalized fashion to allocate staff resources and to serve as a final check on whether proposed regulations are feasible. The comparison has been between monetary costs of control and the amount of pollution emissions prevented. For example, in the late 1950's the District contemplated reducing the permissible level of particulate emissions until it was discovered that it would cost $150 million to reduce daily emissions by only 13 tons. This reduction

was not considered worth the costs.[59] Rule 62 and
the incinerator ban also exemplify the fact that
the District's rules and regulations consider the
economic impact but that this is not their primary
thrust. In most cases, it was decided that particular sources ought to be controlled because they
were identified as being major contributors of pollution, and tentative rules were prepared to do
this. Important considerations have been (1) lack
of technology or (2) the lack of available alternatives. As a general rule, regulations have been
made as strict as existing abatement techniques
would allow. No rule proposed by the District has
been turned down by the County Supervisors because
it was considered too expensive to implement.

The same sort of comparison between monetary
costs of control and amount of emissions reduced
has also been used to evaluate agency performance.
Thus, it is pointed out that the cost to control
5,180 tons of air pollutants per day from stationary
sources has been at least three quarters of a billion dollars and that these figures might be only
half of actual costs.*

---

*Louis J. Fuller, "Air Pollution Control - A
Billion Dollar Problem," APCD news release, April
17, 1969. Another 1,140 tons are controlled by the
installation of crankcase and exhaust control devices
on automobiles. Some of the monetary cost can be
measured with exactness, while the remainder was estimated. For example, the permits issued for pollution control equipment installed in Los Angeles
County contain a record of equipment cost. These
show that industry has spent more than $135 million.
This does not include the cost of maintaining or operating this equipment or the value of the land it
occupies, nor does it take into account the cost of
designing the building into other basic equipment
of modifications necessary to meet District specifications without the use of separate equipment.
Another recorded item is the amount paid for fees
for these permits and the amounts paid as fines for
convictions of violations of District rules. From
1948 to 1967, these totaled $2,875,000. Also known
is the cost of operating the District for 18 years--
$46,095,300, or about $2.6 million per year on the
average. Of this total, $6 million was spent on
basic research. Another item of expense is rubbish

A Position of Power

A very important aspect of the District's strategy has been to develop a "position of power" based on public support, technical knowledge of air pollution and devices and processes for reducing emissions, and a well-defined legal and administrative structure. An early admitted mistake of the District was a failure to acquaint the public with all of its activities.[60] Thus, since the early 1950's, the District has carried on extensive public information programs. Much emphasis has been given to publicly rebutting arguments raised against proposed regulations or the application of existing regulations. In essence, the strategy is to put polluters of the air on the defensive by marshaling public opinion against them. The District does not dissuade "outraged" citizens' groups from having protest meetings and voicing their protests to the company or industry in question. The press and other media are also not discouraged from publishing or disseminating programs that emphasize the role of industry and public utilities in air pollution.[61]

The District's research on control technology allows it to counter potential charges by polluters that proposed regulations are impossible to meet, and its basic research on the effects of air pollution has been a strong incentive for the Board of County Supervisors to pass control regulations even when these have been opposed by important segments of the business community in Los Angeles. A "climate to negotiate" has been created in which the polluter is aware of the high probability that he would lose a court fight and realizes that, even if he should win, he would receive a great deal of adverse publicity. Large industrial firms and public utilities are especially sensitive to such publicity.

One reason this strategy has been applied so successfully is the provision in the District's regulations that a variance cannot be granted where

---

collection and disposal, which costs an estimated $55 million per year in Los Angeles County. Finally, there are the costs of the hearings before the FPC and the court suit challenging the District's constitutionality--more than $250,000.

a showing has been made that a nuisance is present.*
(For example, it was shown that the burning of
high-sulfur oil constituted a nuisance in the immediate vicinity of power plants.) In a typical
case, a polluter would be informed that in a presentation before the District's hearing board the
District staff would present a nuisance argument
and that, once the nuisance is presented, the hearing board would be precluded from granting a variance. The only recourse for the polluter would be
to take the case to Superior Court and have the case
tried before the whole community with the resulting
publicity.[62]

The strategy has been effective to the extent
that, since the passing of Rule 62 in the late
1950's, there has been no significant large-scale
opposition. Since that time, the District and industry have not taken the overt position of being
adversaries. The most significant example of this
change is Rule 66, dealing with the emissions from
solvents. Over a period of years, difficult technological problems were worked out cooperatively,
and the adopted rule turned out to be more stringent
than the original proposal of the District. Even
though the solvent industry is spending a great deal
of money on research in an attempt to prove the rule
ineffective, this form of opposition can be contrasted with earlier opposition based on inadequate
or nonexistent information.

The Sequential Approach to Problems

The District has approached the air pollution
problem in Los Angeles in a sequential manner and
has explicitly or implicitly recongized that all
major decisions are interrelated. Early in the
District's operation, it was believed that sulfur
dioxide was the cause of much of the smog with help
from the ubiquitous back-yard incinerator. Thus,
early major control efforts focused on sources of
sulfur dioxide and these incinerators. The latter
were given emphasis because of the psychological

---

*This has not always been true. Southern
California Edison operated under a variance for
a number of years.

impact of the obvious visible emissions and the
presence of a viable solution at hand (refuse collection and sanitary landfill). The automobile industry also continually advanced the argument that
the back-yard incinerators were the source of most
of the pollution and not the automobile. As noted
before, the removal of the incinerators negated
this argument. At a later date, in arguing against
the WOGA proposal to relate fuel oil burning to
weathèr conditions, the District could state: "It
would be a complete breach of faith to the people
of Los Angeles County who were told that if they
led the way by giving up their back-yard incinerators other sources of pollution would be eliminated."[63] It is probably difficult to overestimate
the importance to the District of having been able
to point to other large investments in control processes when proposing new regulations and enforcing
existing ones. Remaining polluters cannot fail to
see the crude equity that is involved.

The Role of Bargaining

Operating from their position of power, the
District has always proposed to the Board of County
Commissioners the strongest regulation--i.e., the
most restrictive in light of available technology--
it thought could be justified. To date, no proposed regulation has failed to be enacted by the
Commissioners. Thus, formal bargaining in the adoption of regulations has not taken place.* These
rules have been applied both within the spirit and
the letter of the law. This has been possible because the District has always had a large enforcement staff.

Within the bargaining framework outlined earlier
it seems that significant conflict resolution takes
place within the context of the informal conferences
the District employs extensively. At the District

---

*Although formal bargaining is precluded by the
agency's charter, one Los Angeles official candidly
admitted that on occasion "deals" had been made with
polluters, but they played a minor role in the over-
all pollution control program and, in any case,
could not be revealed.

offices, views, positions, and information are ex-
changed with industry representatives. At this
level, incrementalism, ritualization, continuing
negotiation, and the determination of focal point
solutions all play a part.* This factor, not obvious
in the chronological development of issues emphasized in the case study, cannot be given too much
importance.

The Political and Institutional Framework

Both the issues of burning natural gas and
low-sulfur oil, not to mention the federal jurisdiction over emission control devices, emphasize
the fact that some significant decisions in air
pollution control are beyond the control of the
Los Angeles Air Pollution Control District. When
higher levels of government have the responsibility,
conflict between a state or federal functional
agency's multiple objectives has in the past typically resulted in the downgrading of the relatively
new objective of environmental quality. This has
been particularly evident in the actions of the
Federal Power Commission, which has been more concerned with pipeline management than air pollution
control. The District's solution to this problem
is Presidential leadership in changing administrative priorities.[64]

At the opposite end of the scale, industrial
interests in Southern California have continually
complained that they have been unable to obtain
fair and impartial due process before the District's
hearing board and the County Supervisors and that
proceedings of the board have been conducted in an
"atmosphere of hysteria." The California Manufacturers Association also has stated in the past that air
pollution control in the Los Angeles Basin is based
on politics rather than economics. Indeed, the
Association has been criticized by Los Angeles newspaper columnists for fighting their battles on the
wrong terms, for it continually asked a group of
nonscientists--the Board of Supervisors--to rule on
extremely technical arguments. There is some logic
to the industry argument that the board was making
political decisions rather than technical ones,

*See Chapter 7 for more detail on this matter.

particularly if one considers their interpretation
of the public interest as an essentially political
decision.

NOTES

1. L. Herber, Crisis in our Cities (Englewood
Cliffs, N.J.: Prentice-Hall, 1965), p. 50.

2. Ibid.

3. Air Pollution Control District Act,
California Health and Safety Code, Sections 24198-
24323 (West, 1967).

4. H. Kennedy, "The History, Legal and Admin-
istrative Aspects of Air Pollution Control in the
County of Los Angeles" (Report submitted to the
Board of Supervisors of the County of Los Angeles,
May 9, 1954), pp. 12-14.

5. Ibid.

6. Ibid.

7. APCD news release, August 29, 1957.

8. For a short history of air pollution from
automobiles in Los Angeles, see Herber, op. cit.,
pp. 48-55.

9. Kennedy, op. cit., p. 66.

10. Ibid.

11. Air Pollution Control District Report,
October, 1957, p. 1.

12. Kennedy, op. cit.

13. Ibid., 55.

14. APCD Report, op. cit.

15. Interview with Robert Barsky, APCD Deputy
Air Pollution Control Officer, August, 1968.

16.   Interview with Arthur Atkisson, Institute
of Urban Ecology, University of Southern California,
August, 1967.

17.   The sources for the following sections
include interviews with Robert Barsky, APCD Deputy
Air Pollution Control Officer; and David Mix,
Assistant County Counsel, County of Los Angeles;
Los Angeles area newspapers; and unpublished infor-
mation in the files of the Air Pollution Control
District.   Specific references are as noted below.

18.   Los Angeles Herald, October 10, 1958.

19.   Los Angeles Examiner, November 14, 1958.

20.   Ibid.

21.   Los Angeles Times Mirror, December 17, 1958.

22.   Ibid.

23.   Los Angeles Herald and Express, January 5,
1959.

24.   Los Angeles Times, April 8, 1959; Los
Angeles Examiner, May 12, 1959; Western Oils, July
15, 1959.

25.   Western Oils, loc. cit.

26.   Ibid.

27.   Los Angeles Mirror News, October 20, 1959.

28.   APCD news release, December 8, 1959.

29.   Los Angeles Mirror News, December 2, 1959;
Los Angeles Times, December 2, 1959; Oil and Gas
Journal, December 4, 1959.

30.   Los Angeles Mirror News, June 27, 1959;
Los Angeles Times, June 24, 1959; Pacific Oil
Marketer, June-July, 1960.

31.   Smith Griswold, APCD Officer, "Testimony
Regarding the Amendments to Rule 62 Proposed by the
Western Oil and Gas Association," August 9, 1959;
APCD news release, August 9, 1959.

32. APCD news release, August 9, 1959.

33. Los Angeles Examiner, July 8, 1960.

34. Ibid.

35. Pasadena Star News, July 9, 1960.

36. Ibid., March 23, 1961; Los Angeles Examiner,
March 17, 1961.

37. Ibid.

38. Interview with Robert Barsky and David
Mix, August, 1968.

39. Interview with Robert Barsky, August, 1968.

40. Los Angeles Times, March 5, 1961. Most
of the gas at this time and later came from Texas.

41. Ibid.

42. Los Angeles Herald Examiner, January 8,
1962.

43. Interviews with Robert Barsky and David
Mix, August, 1968.

44. A summary of Federal Power Commission
records by the Western Oil and Gas Association,
Westchester Citizen, January 31, 1963.

45. Oil Daily, March 11, 1963.

46. APCD news release, June 2, 1965; Oil Daily,
May 28, 1965.

47. Ibid.

48. Interview with David Mix.

49. Los Angeles Times, December 12, 1965.

50. Ibid.

51. Selected verbatim statements from introduction of FPC Opinion No. 500, July 26, 1966.

52. Interviews with Robert Barsky and David Mix.

53. New York Times, July 18, 1967.

54. Interview with Robert Barsky.

55. Interview with David Mix.

56. The best history of this development is found in U.S. Senate, Air Pollution - 1967; Automobile Air Pollution, Hearings before the Subcommittee on Air and Water Pollution of the Committee on Public Works, 90th Cong., 1st Sess., Part 1, February, 1967.

57. Ibid.

58. Interview with Robert Barsky.

59. Interview with David Mix.

60. Kennedy, op. cit., p. 1.

61. Interview with Robert Barsky.

62. Interviews with Robert Barsky and David Mix.

63. Unpublished testimony by Smith Griswold before the Board of County Supervisors.

64. Interview with Robert Barsky.

CHAPTER **6** DECISION-MAKING
IN AIR QUALITY
MANAGEMENT IN
NEW YORK CITY

Air pollution control in New York City has a
longer but more sporadic history than Los Angeles.
During the early part of this century, the New
York Sanitary Code prohibited the emission of dense
smoke and cinders, dust, or gas, but although a
smoke control unit within the Department of Health
existed briefly during the 1930's, not until after
World War II did air pollution control have any
status in city government.[1] An ineffectual Bureau
of Smoke Control created after the War within the
Department of Housing and Buildings became an independent department in 1952, with powers to (a) li-
cense all equipment that could cause objectionable
emissions and (b) require alterations in existing
equipment in order to secure compliance with any
rules and regulations that might be adopted.[2] From
1952 to 1965, there occurred a slow but steady development of rules and regulations by the department.[3]

The recognition that air pollution control involved more than mechanical smoke control had
prompted the creation in 1952 of the separate Department of Air Pollution Control and a Board of
Air Pollution Control. The following 13 years saw
a growing concern with air pollution in general and
for the problem of the on-site incinerators in particular. Under mounting pressure from the U.S. Department of Health, Education and Welfare and
Citizens for Clean Air (a public pressure group composed of fairly influential New York City citizens),
the City Council started to react in 1965. A Special Committee on Air Pollution of the City Council,
chaired by Councilman Robert Low, was formed and
shortly thereafter released a rather comprehensive
report dealing with air pollution in New York City.[4]

The report noted, among other things, that the city's range for levels of suspended particulates in the air was higher than any other major U.S. city and that the annual city-wide dustfall averages, little changed from 1952, were 60 tons per square mile per month, with the Manhattan average at 80 tons per square mile per month.[5] The city also had a higher average of sulfur dioxide and higher maximum sulfur dioxide values than any other major city in the country.

A number of public hearings dealing with air pollution control were held before the council committee after the release of this report. The report and these hearings emphasized that the most significant sources of air pollution in New York City were on-site incineration of refuse, municipal incineration, and combustion of fuel for space heating and electricity generation purposes. Whereas there is little heavy industry within the city, industrial emissions were not considered to be important sources of air pollution, and the reduction of automobile emissions was also given low priority due to the magnitude of the contributions of other polluters.

The result of these hearings was the introduction of a control bill in the City Council by Councilman Low in early 1966. The bill dealt with the reduction of sulfur dioxide emissions from fuel burning, the gradual elimination of bituminous coal use, the upgrading of municipal and existing private on-site incinerators, and the banning of refuse incineration in new buildings.

The major source of sulfur dioxide at this time was the combustion of bituminous coal and residual (Number 6) fuel oil. Consolidated Edison, a large public utility, was burning approximately one half of the fuel consumed in the city and during a minimum space-heating day (summer) was contributing almost all of the sulfur dioxide in the atmosphere. This contribution fell to about 25 per cent during a maximum heating day (winter). Fuel use for space heating in commercial, institutional, large apartment houses, and small residential buildings accounted for virtually all of the sulfur dioxide emissions not attributable to Con Ed. The proposed bill did not specify emission levels for sulfur dioxide but required the use of low-sulfur fuels to attain lower rates of pollution emissions.

Municipal incinerators were at this time generating about 20 per cent (4,350 tons per year) of the particulate matter in the air over Manhattan. The Low proposal specified that no municipal incinerator could be operated after May 30, 1969, unless modern air pollution control devices were installed. Approximately 12,000 apartment house and commercial incinerators were also emitting an estimated 8,400 to 9,000 tons of particulates per year into the atmosphere. The bill required that they be "upgraded" through the installation of emission control equipment.

A few months before this bill was introduced, newly elected Mayor John Lindsay, who had campaigned on a platform of clean air, set up a special Task Force on Air Pollution under the chairmanship of Norman Cousins. The report of this task force,[6] although made public after the bill became law, had considerable influence on the Mayor's view of the proposed legislation. In a presentation before the City Council, the Mayor asked that the requirement of a specific kind of control device for incinerators be stricken from the bill.[7] His position was that installation of proper monitoring devices for the continuous recording of emissions from smokestacks would make it unnecessary to specify the kind of control equipment to keep the emissions within the prescribed standard. This view was probably derived from Cousins' Task Force recommendation that companies like Consolidated Edison, the major public utility in the city, be given a free hand in their control equipment. This proposal was criticized by council members as being "too long range," not resulting in immediate improvement in air quality.[8] The councilmen also thought that it would be too vast a job to monitor either individual smokestacks or even groups of them, a typical statement being that "if a plant is told what equipment to use, its emissions will be safe."[9] Another criticism was that there was no evidence that such devices were available.

In late March of 1966, the council passed the bill unanimously. At this stage, the bill was the result of sixteen months of deliberations. A month later, Cousins' report was officially released to the public. It called the air over New York City the most polluted of any major U.S. city and, although suggesting the consideration of alternatives

to on-site incineration, recommended that all existing apartment house incinerators be upgraded in
the same manner required by the bill. Mayor Lindsay
signed the bill in May, 1966, and it was immediately
labeled by the New York Times as the most stringent
air pollution legislation in the country.10

During most of the deliberations on the bill,
which became known as Local Law 14, public concern
and interest was at a high level. Playing a considerable part in the development of this concern
was the Citizens for Clean Air group. The organization provided technical information on air pollution
to its own members and other civic organizations
and held a series of technical workshops. A
speaker's bureau was also organized, and representatives of the organization took part in televised
forums and radio interviews and testified in public
hearings. Although not in full swing until after
Local Law 14 was passed, particularly significant
in the building of public concern was a multimedia
advertising campaign by Citizens for Clean Air
which included a full-page advertisement in Life
magazine and newspaper and television advertise-
ments. The organization thus had a considerable,
though indirect, role in the passing of Local Law
14.

Somewhat surprisingly, the Commissioner of
Air Pollution Control who would implement the law
did not play a part in its formulation. The Mayor
had not yet filled the position when the bill was
being considered, the former commissioner having
resigned after assisting in the development of the
legislation. The new commissioner, Austin Heller,
did not join the department until July, 1966, and
was thus presented with a law to enforce over which
he had had no influence. Mayor Lindsay, without a
large technical staff at his command, relied on the
published Cousins' report for guidance. The law,
then, was primarily the responsibility of the City
Council and Councilman Low. The council, partly
because of the recent change in city administration,
bore the brunt of increasing public pressure for
action on air pollution and reacted by producing
Local Law 14.

Some months after the bill was passed, the City
accepted the classification of a C-3 region by the
New York State Air Pollution Control Board. This

established ambient air quality objectives in New
York City for the more common air contaminants including sulfur dioxide and suspended and settleable
particulates. For suspended particulates, the median values for 24-hour samples must be less than
80 micrograms per cubic meter, and 84 per cent of
the 24-hour samples must also be less than 120
micrograms per cubic meter. For 30-day sampling
periods, the median value for settleable particulates must be less than 0.90 milligrams per square
centimeter; 84 per cent of the values must also be
less than 1.20 milligrams per square centimeter
over the same 30-day period. The ambient air quality objective for sulfur dioxide was set at 0.1
ppm as a 24-hour average, with a maximum of 0.25
ppm for 1 hour. On an annual basis, these values
may be exceeded not more than 1 per cent of the
time.* The City agreed to meet these objectives
in five years with the qualification that they were
viewed as minimal standards by the City and therefore no more than guides to follow.**

THE ON-SITE INCINERATION ISSUE

Because the developments relating to air pollution control in New York City after the passage
of Local Law 14 are considerable, this chapter deals

---

*New York Department of Health, "Board of Air
Pollution Control Ambient Air Quality Objectives--
Classification System," 1964. The primary means of
achieving the ambient air quality objective for sulfur dioxide was the limitation of the sulfur content
of fuel. Under the provisions of Local Law 14, no
coal or residual fuel oil with sulfur content of
greater than 2.2 per cent could be used within the
city as of January 20, 1967. After May, 1969, the
sulfur content was to drop to a flat 2 per cent.
After May, 1971, permissible level would be 1 per
cent. This timetable was moved up considerably
through an agreement between the Department of Air
Pollution Control and Consolidated Edison less than
a year later.

**These objectives were viewed as judgmental
because they were necessarily based on inadequate
data that did not consider in detail synergistic
effects.

mainly with the on-site incineration of refuse, an
issue that demonstrates in microcosm most of the
factors involved in air quality management in a
large metropolitan area. As such, references to
other aspects of air pollution control in New York
City will be made only as they relate to the on-site
incineration issue.[11]

The on-site incineration of refuse in apartment houses and businesses in New York City is a
relatively recent phenomenon. Prior to 1951, such
incinerators were not required, but in that year
the city's building code was amended to require
that all new multiple dwellings install incinerators.
Thus, from this time until 1966, when the administrative code was again changed, the trend was toward more on-site incinerator installations. During
this period, the City estimated that, as more and
more of the apartment buildings built before 1951
(most of which had no incinerators) were torn down
and replaced by multiple-dwelling units with incinerators, the need for municipal incineration
would decline. Prior to 1966, the long-range goal
was the gradual elimination of its municipal incinerators or, at the very least, reducing municipal
incineration to a minor role. The on-site incinerator requirement, of course, reduced the City's
costs not only for incineration but also for refuse
collection.

Section 892-4.3 of Local Law 14 stated that
all apartment houses except those of six stories
or less were required to have an upgraded incinerator within one year of the passage of the bill.
Starting two years after the bill's passage, multiple dwellings of six stories or less were also required to have upgraded incinerators. The process
of upgrading included the "installation and use of
an auxiliary gas burner regulated by automatic fir-
ing clocks, an overfire air fan and nozzle system
and control apparatus as may be determined by the
commissioner."[12] Section 893-3.0 stated that two
years after the bill was passed "no person shall
cause or permit the installation or construction
of refuse burning equipment for the burning of garbage or other waste material."[13] Thus, even though
incinerators in existing buildings had to upgrade,
incinerators of any type were not to be installed
in new or existing buildings after May, 1968. This
emphasis on upgrading seems to have originated in a

1959 study by the College of Engineering of New
York University, which indicated that a significant
reduction in particulate emissions from on-site
incinerators could result from the use of automatic
operational procedures mentioned above and the use
of a scrubber system--a motor-driven device to
force the smoke through a special water bath that
will remove the heavy particulates.[14]

Whereas Local Law 14 specified that the commissioner was to determine the type of control
equipment to be used, one of the first significant
acts of the new Commissioner of Air Pollution Control was to hold hearings on design standards used
in upgrading incinerators. Requirements in existence when he came to office were found to be insufficient in that they would reduce particulate
emissions by only 65 per cent. Even though Councilman Low accused Commissioner Heller of "foot dragging," the Board of Air Pollution Control rejected
the existing design standards which had been developed by the previous commissioner and another set
was developed that specified a 90 per cent reduction
in particulate emissions. At a hearing held on
these requirements, a few representatives of citizens'
groups were very vocal in their support of stringent
requirements, but they were greatly outnumbered by
the real-estate interests who requested that the
City ease the new requirements or delay their enforcement. (By this time--fall, 1966--some apartment building landlords were becoming openly critical
of the fact that detailed instructions for the required incinerator upgrading were not available.)
A key argument of the opposition, presented by a
representative of the Incinerator Institute of America, was that the job of upgrading on-site incinerators in the alloted time was not possible because
there were few incinerator manufacturers who could
supply.the necessary equipment locally in the time
available.[15] This argument was seemingly countered
when a few manufacturers tried to sell their products on the spot. The Department of Air Pollution
Control argued that an extension was just an excuse
for doing nothing. The regulations were adopted
by the Board of Air Pollution Control in January,
1967.[16]

Whereas Local Law 14 required that all on-site
incinerators be upgraded, the City Office of Administration some months after the law was passed

requested that the various city departments operating buildings estimate the cost of upgrading their
incinerators. The City Housing Authority expressed
doubt that it could meet the deadline required by
the law (eight months hence) due to the time necessary to raise funds, prepare contracts, and have
the work completed. The Office of Administration
also found that cost estimates of the various departments for upgrading varied considerably, and
city officials decided to establish a committee of
city department representatives to study the economic aspects of the problem. This committee was
divided into two task forces dealing with the economics of upgrading and the equipment used for
upgrading. At this time, serious attention was
first given to whether on-site incinerators built
before 1951, and therefore voluntarily constructed,
could be legally forced to upgrade rather than
shut down operation.

A confidential draft report prepared by this
committee using City Housing Authority data found
that the average cost for upgrading on-site incinerators might vary between $6,500 and $8,200,
not including financing costs (Table I).[17] Note
was made of the fact that some small building
owners would have difficulty getting loans to pay
for the improvements. The annual cost of operation including a ten-year equipment depreciation
schedule was estimated to range from $1,375 to
$2,480. The report concluded:

> The need for owners of thousands of
> buildings to upgrade their inciner-
> ators by May 1967 and many other
> owners by May 1968 constitutes a
> crash program of such magnitude as
> to defeat the intent of the legisla-
> tion. Not only will necessary equip-
> ment, instruments, and parts be
> difficult or even impossible to ob-
> tain, but the great demand on suppli-
> ers and contractors will boom prices
> way above the costs given herein. . . .
> A very limited number of qualified
> installers and contractors are en-
> gaged in the business of installing
> and upgrading incinerators. When the
> rush to upgrade incinerators begins,
> many small and fringe companies and

individuals qualified or not will be
able to secure contracts and jobs.
Despite city inspections, many inadequate and faulty installations can
be expected.18

TABLE 1

Average Incinerator Upgrading Costs,
New York City

1)	Providing auxiliary gas burner, time clocks, overfire air system		$1,500.00
2)	Special requirements, enlarged grate, enlarged hearths, spark arrester, etc.	0 to	700.00
3)	Roof scrubber--providing a scrubber, housing heating, plumbing, electrical work		5,000.00
4)	Structural support for scrubber	0 to	1,000.00
	Total	$6,500 to	8,200.00

Source: Mayor's Office of Administration, New
York City, Report of Task Force No. 1 of the Committee on Implementation of Local Law 14, November 28,
1966, p. 2. (Mimeographed.)

Emphasis was given to the fact that the required
upgrading would impose serious hardships on owners
of small buildings, particularly where incinerators
served less than 30 dwelling units, and to such possibilities as the closing of buildings or the forced
removal of tenants because of high rents unless the
stated requirements were relaxed. Among the proposals given brief mention to relieve the hardship
were (a) omitting the requirement of scrubbers for
incinerators serving few apartments, (b) a lower

standard for particulate emissions from small buildings, and (c) the removal of refuse without incineration.

Two alternatives were discussed in some detail
in the report--utilizing existing incinerator chutes
to convey refuse to basements for transfer to the
sidewalk cans in an unburned and uncompacted condition and collecting refuse at each floor for transfer to the basement and then to curbs unburned and
uncompacted.[19] Although compaction of refuse was
required in new buildings under Local Law 14, it was
not mentioned as a viable alternative at this time
due to Building Department requirements (which were
later lowered) which included metal-lined chutes,
fire-proof compactor rooms, and sprinklers at every
floor. Even though this report ended up supporting
on-site incineration as the cheapest alternative for
the individual landlord, it did not receive extensive public circulation, possibly due to its generally critical nature.*

THE STATUS OF THE INCINERATOR BAN
IN EARLY 1967

Seven months after the passage of Local Law 14,
the status of the incinerator upgrading provision
of the law was unclear. The city administration had
learned that the city's corporation counsel would
shortly rule that Local Law 14 would allow the
owners of on-site incinerators installed before they
were made mandatory in 1951--an unknown number of
incinerators but possibly 50 per cent of the total--

---

*As noted earlier, the annual cost for upgrading
was estimated to be from $1,375 to $2,480, using a
ten-year equipment depreciation schedule. The alternative of utilizing existing refuse chutes for
collection purposes was estimated to cost from
$3,389 to $3,489 annually, due in part to additional
labor costs to remove the refuse from the building
but mainly to rigid requirements that would require
a $7,000 stainless steel refuse chute liner which
pushed the cost of building alteration to almost
$10,000. The average annual cost of converting to
the floor-by-floor refuse collection alternative
could also rise due to the large labor requirements.

to shut down voluntarily if they so desired. This
decision created a great deal of concern as it was
anticipated that the city would be burdened with
considerable unexpected costs. It seems that the
City Council's Committee on Air Pollution, antici-
pating just such an eventuality and the resulting
sudden heavy addition to the load of refuse handled
by the Department of Sanitation, recommended that
a charge be levied against any building owner who
operated an incinerator on or after January 1, 1965,
and who subsequently abandoned it. This charge
would cover collection and disposal costs. Local
Law 14 included a provision designed to effect this,
but the city's corporation counsel felt that, because a key phrase was omitted, pre-1951 buildings
could abandon their incinerators and have the Department of Sanitation collect the unburned refuse
free of charge.

The various city agencies involved in the problem of incinerator upgrading had taken very different stands regarding the feasibility of enforcing
the law. Both the City Council and the Department
of Air Pollution Control expressed the opinion that
most building owners could comply with the law, but,
whereas the City Council was quite consistent in
listing the total number of apartment house incinerators at 12,000, the Department of Air Pollution
Control had at different times given different estimates of the total number and felt that a definite
figure would be arrived at only after a special
building-by-building survey had been completed.[20]
An opposite view of the feasibility of compliance
was taken by the Rent and Rehabilitation Administration and the Department of Sanitation. Rent and
Rehabilitation thought it was too early to make any
prediction regarding the rate of compliance, and the
Department of Sanitation expressed the pessimistic
opinion that due to problems with the law itself
almost all incinerators would eventually be abandoned and predicted that it would be faced with handling a large amount of additional refuse.

Five months after signing the law, Mayor Lindsay
appointed a 50-member New York Business Advisory
Council for Cleaner Air to provide him with information on the economic aspects of air pollution abatement efforts. This council, composed of leading New
York businessmen, never really made any progress,

and it was clear in a short time that the organization would be able to offer little assistance to the
city administration.

The design standards for upgrading incinerators
which had been formally approved and distributed to
landlords were being roundly criticized, not because
of the nature of the requirements but because of the
date of their release. Real-estate interests said
that it had taken too long to find out exactly what
they were expected to do, even though the nature of
the requirements had been made public some months
earlier. Even with the prior knowledge, the landlords had only seven months until the upgrading was
to be completed. The New York Real Estate Board was
calling the deadline for upgrading incinerators unrealistic and urged a two-year extension. The Department of Air Pollution Control countered with a
request for apartment house owners and managers of
buildings seven stories and over to submit reports
on their plans to meet the May 20, 1967, deadline.

The Department also stated publicly that an investigation on their part showed that incinerator
manufacturers and installers were available to do
the work. But, because their number was not large,
a conference was held to which incinerator installers
and manufacturers were invited. This conference did
stimulate interest in the potential market in New
York City, although the city administration realized
that serious problems were involved in getting the
upgrading completed by any time near the May deadline.

A larger meeting, the Conference on Interstate
Air Pollution in the New York-New Jersey Metropolitan Area, also drew the attention of many New Yorkers
in early 1967. Convened by the U.S. Public Health
Service at the request of New York Governor Nelson
Rockefeller, it was sponsored by the Public Health
Service, New York City, and the states involved.
The proceedings dealt with the economic costs and
health effects of air pollution, particularly sulfur
oxides. The annual cost of air pollution in the 17-
county metropolitan area was estimated to be $3
billion, or an average of $620.00 per family per
year.[21] The burden of the testimony of health authorities who spoke at the conference was that there
is a direct relationship between air pollution and
various respiratory ailments.[22]

Early 1967 also saw the corporation counsel officially release an opinion that all incinerators
installed before 1951, when they were first made mandatory, could be shut down if the building owners so
desired. This development led to a charge by building owners who still had to upgrade that the law was
discriminatory. Commissioner Heller supported the
corporation counsel's interpretation, however, reasoning that it would result in the shutting down of
the oldest and least efficient incinerators and thus
would be desirable from an air pollution abatement
point of view.*

THE CITY AGENCIES AND LOCAL LAW 14

As the May, 1967, deadline for incinerator upgrading approached, the Task Force to Implement Local
Law 14 met to consider the practicability of developing a fact sheet on apartment house incinerators
for use by city agencies in answering inquiries in
connection with Local Law 14 from owners, tenants,
and other parties, and possibly for dissemination
for publicity purposes. At this meeting, it was suggested that a position paper be prepared by the task
force recommending changes in Local Law 14, but this
was not done because no city official appeared willing to sponsor even minor amendments to the existing
law. It was agreed that a fact sheet must deal with
the law as it was regardless of the problems involved. This fact sheet was released in early
April. An associated action was the issuance of an
administrative order by the city administration di-
recting all city agencies to conform to the incinerator upgrading provisions of Local Law 14 and to
make a report by May 20.

INTER-AGENCY CONFLICTS

Due to a lengthening series of disagreements
between the Mayor and the Commissioner of Sanitation,

---

*The confidential report by the task force on
the economics of implementing Local Law 14, which
had been highly critical of the law, was leaked to
the press by an unidentified source at this time.
New York Times, February 21, 1967.

the working relationship between the departments
of Air Pollution Control and Sanitation was not
good.   The Commissioner of Sanitation was openly
critical of the aspects of Local Law 14 that dealt
with refuse handling and disposal.

The Commissioner of Air Pollution Control, in
preparing to enforce the law, had no authority to
require compliance before the May 20 deadline.   The
only alternatives open to him were to seal every
noncomplying incinerator on May 20 or to expedite
compliance after that date.   Although he chose the
latter option, he announced that the on-site incinerators that failed to meet the May 20 deadline for
installation of upgrading equipment would be "sealed
in five days."[23]   He also stated that about half the
city's landlords had indicated that they "intended
to comply with the law."[24]   Those landlords whose
incinerators were sealed would be subject to a
$25.00-a-day fine from the date of sealing and would
be billed for the cost of the garbage collection by
the Sanitation Department.[25]   But the Commissioner
of Sanitation was saying at the same time that he
was not sure how the City was going to handle the
added load of refuse collection if many incinerators
were sealed.[26]

The President of the City Council and the Commissioner of Sanitation announced that they thought
it impossible for apartment owners to meet the May
20 deadline because of engineering, manufacturing,
and installation time required.[27]   The Commissioner
of Sanitation also said that his department could
not handle refuse from the incinerators that were
allowed to shut down under the law and noted that
even the eleven Department of Sanitation incinerators
would not be upgraded by the 1969 deadline required
by Local Law 14.   The Department of Air Pollution
Control was still insistent on compliance by the
deadline, although the Commissioner of Air Pollution
Control said he would accept applications for proposed conversions as evidence of compliance.

THE FAILURE OF THE
UPGRADING REQUIREMENT

On May 6, the City mailed postcards to 32,000
real-estate owners reminding them that they were required to have an incinerator operating certificate
by May 20.   Concurrently, the Executive Committee

of the 3,400-member New York City Real Estate
Board voted to take legal action to try to block
enforcement of regulations on upgrading. Board members complained that pleas for guidance and information from the Department of Air Pollution Control
had met with "delays and indecisive answers" and
said that 99 per cent of the on-site incinerators
would be outlawed eventually and one could not justify an expenditure if it would be outdated in one
year.[28]

A week before the deadline, the Commissioner of
Air Pollution Control was saying that he would accept
assurance that a contract had been signed as evidence
of compliance and was considering a plan to ease
compliance by letting landlords put up a cash depos-
it signifying their intentions to comply with the
regulations. By that time, owners of 1,300 to 1,400
of what were now estimated to be approximately
4,200 incinerators that had to meet the May 20 deadline for upgrading had given an "indication of compliance." A day before the deadline, the City
started to give more ground on the compliance requirement. More than 100 landlords who told the Department of Sanitation they were shutting their
incinerators down were told by telegram to continue
incineration until the Department could arrange for
garbage pickup. At that time, it was decided that
the 4,000 "voluntary" buildings which were eligible
to shut down would have an extension of 10-24 days
before discontinuing.[29] The 4,000 to 5,000 incinerators in the upgrading group were not affected by
the order. The telegram was sent partly because
the Department of Sanitation did not know how much
refuse there would be to pick up. This 10-day extension eventually became an indefinite extension.

On the first day of enforcement of the law,
there were charges by Councilman Low that the Lindsay
Administration was "foot dragging" and "bungling" in
enforcing the law.[30] Low specifically charged that
the city administration had created confusion by
issuing guidelines suggesting that even upgraded
incinerators might be shut down the following May
and that the city administration had made no request
of the Bureau of the Budget for an increase in the
Sanitation Department budget to handle the added
load. At the same time, the lawsuit had been filed

by the real-estate interests contesting the consti-
tutionality of the law on the grounds that it was
arbitrary and capricious and did not apply equally
to all polluters of the air. This suit had the effect of sharply limiting the public statements that
could be made by the city administration on aspects
of the law.

Out of a total of 300 inspections during the
first day of enforcement, 200 violations were found.
About 1,400 notices of violation were sent during
the first month after enforcement started. It soon
became evident that the greatest activity in the
submission of formal notices to discontinue incineration and applications for upgrading took place
just prior to and shortly after the date of compliance. By July, the Department of Air Pollution Control estimated that 75 per cent of the building
owners had submitted either their applications to
upgrade, their contracts to upgrade, or their applications to shut down in the case of the older buildings, and the Department of Air Pollution Control
considered their program of compliance to be increasingly successful after an admittedly shaky
start. But every time someone submitted an application to discontinue, they were sent a telegram
signed by the commissioners of Sanitation and Air
Pollution Control stating that they were to continue
incineration until the Sanitation Department could
pick up their refuse. Commissioner Heller signed
the telegram with the agreement that an investigation of the premises called for in the telegram
would be made within 10 days--the 10 days mentioned
in the violation notice which was served to incinerator owners. This agreement was not honored by
the Department of Sanitation; not a single building
that had applied to shut down was ever approved to
do so during this period. Approximately 90 incinerators had been sealed by mid-summer, but 55 were
allowed to reopen when owners submitted evidence of
initial steps of compliance to the Department of
Air Pollution Control. Only two incinerators had
been upgraded to the required specifications.

These developments were the start of the stand-
still in the enforcement program after the first
month of what the Department of Air Pollution Control considered to be promising cooperation. It

was now a widespread rumor among the real-estate
interests that the Department of Sanitation was not
going to pick up the refuse from closed down incinerators, thereby giving them a convenient excuse
for not proceeding with upgrading. It was the opinion of the Department of Air Pollution Control at
this time that it was imperative from an enforcement
point of view that the Department of Sanitation pick
up the refuse of a few buildings that opted to shut
down in order to demonstrate the commitment of the
city administration to enforce the law. This was
not done. Another factor was the prerogative of
building owners to deny access to their premises
to city investigators under a recent decision of
the U.S. Supreme Court.

The Commissioner of Air Pollution Control had
stated publicly that the desirable long-term solution to the problem of reducing air pollution from
incineration was the encouragement of more efficient
municipal incineration or solid waste disposal and
that the on-site incineration aspect of Local Law
14 was meant to deal with the more immediate problems.[31] This statement was possibly perceived by
many landlords to mean that incinerators might soon
be obsolete, and they thus had a ready excuse for
not proceeding with haste to upgrade.

The enforcement program was finally brought to
a halt by indirect action on the part of the City
Council and the city administration. During mid-
July, the Building Committee of the City Council,
the same committee that reported out Local Law 14,
reported out a new housing code which rescinded the
requirement that incinerators be maintained in
buildings. The code was passed by the council and
signed by the Mayor. The lack of a clear statement
on on-site incineration resulted in an interpretation by the corporation counsel that all on-site
incinerators could now be considered voluntary, meaning that all such incinerators now had the option
to shut down.

A CHANGE IN THE LAW

Two months after the May 20 deadline, it was
clear to all parties concerned that changes in Local

Law 14 were inevitable. Mayor Lindsay asked
for revisions that would make the law "workable."
Councilman Low, its original sponsor, said he would
introduce an amendment to the law because its original intent of requiring upgrading had been sub-
verted. In a status report regarding on-site
incineration,[32] the Department of Air Pollution
Control--in addition to calling attention to a lack
of cooperation on the part of the Department of
Sanitation, which was not prepared to pick up the
added refuse from those buildings whose incinerators
were being shut down--came out against proposed
amendments to the law that would continue to force
the mandatory on-site incinerator upgrading.*

Because the law had been largely the work of
the City Council, the Mayor was open to suggestions
that he was not to blame for the law's defects and
that it would not be contradictory for him to pro-
pose changes in it. He had at this time just received from a consulting firm a report on using a
systems approach in city administration.[33] The incinerator issue had been used by the firm to demonstrate the potential of this approach, and the
report concluded that it would be desirable to
change the law. Basing his action on the recommendations of this report and those of the Department
of Air Pollution Control, the Mayor proposed that
all on-site incinerators have the opportunity to
shut down. His action at this time can be viewed
in the context of achieving tangible results in air
pollution control by the time of the next city elec-
tion in November, 1969. The Department of Air Pollution Control, reflecting the view of most city
departments, came out for giving options to either
upgrade, compact, or discontinue incineration, while

---

*In the report, note was made of the fact that
the corporation counsel's interpretation making all
incinerators voluntary would be in keeping with a
desirable policy of going to energy conversion systems. The advantages of such a system were listed
as being that sulfur-free refuse is used as a fuel
for generating steam and electricity rather than
wasted as unused energy and that 12,000 to 14,000
low-level sources of pollution are eliminated which
otherwise would require surveillance by a large City-
financed staff of inspectors and engineers.

Councilman Low's committee believed the emphasis should still be on upgrading. The Department of Sanitation, although favoring the use of options, also favored some continued on-site incineration in order to keep refuse removal costs within "reasonable bounds."

Discussions were carried out between affected city departments and real-estate representatives on possible changes in the law. At a meeting of the Task Force on Implementing Local Law 14 that followed these discussions, a suggestion arose that existing apartment buildings be placed in three categories-- (1) under 12 apartments per incinerator, from which uncompacted refuse would be collected by the Department of Sanitation; (2) over 49 apartments per incinerator, which would be permitted to upgrade incinerators; and (3) the intermediate group of from 13 to 49 apartments per incinerator, which would be permitted to upgrade incinerators or to install compactors. Real-estate representatives, however, said that all large buildings should have the choice of upgrading or installing compactors. Mandating the installation of compactors in intermediate buildings was discussed at length, but the majority of the task force believed that the cost of handling uncompacted refuse would force many owners to install compactors. A plan was also suggested that would reduce the cost of incinerator upgrading to small building owners. A building having 20 or less apartments per incinerator would be allowed to omit installing a scrubber but would be required to comply with all other parts of the upgrading criteria. About 65 per cent of the particulates would be removed under this plan, and the cost was deemed to be "reasonable."

A report produced by the inter-departmental task force on the economics of upgrading or discontinuing incineration came out in favor of allowing building owners a free choice in methods of reducing air pollution from on-site incinerators because "when building owners carefully analyze the comparative total cost of available methods, they will act not only to their own advantage, but also in the best interests of the city."[34] The three means of abating air pollution from on-site incinerators discussed were (1) upgrading existing incinerators, (2) discontinuing

incineration and compacting the unburned refuse,
and (3) discontinuing incineration and placing uncompacted refuse for collection. Using cost data
from the Housing Authority and other city agencies
that considered the varying size of buildings, operating expenses, labor costs, capital investment,
and the distribution of unit costs among a number
of apartments, the task force came up with the results shown in Figure 1. The graph indicates that
the larger buildings would find it most economical
to upgrade, the middle-sized buildings could make a
decision themselves whether to compact or to upgrade, and that the smallest buildings would discontinue incineration and handle uncompacted ref-
use.35

By November, 1967, two competing amendments to
Local Law 14 were pending before the City Council.
Intro 470, as it was called, was introduced by
Councilman Low and would mandate that every incinerator in operation after January, 1965, must either
upgrade, at a cost of from $6,000 to $10,000, or
convert to compacting equipment in a two-stage procedure at a cost of from $5,000 to $6,000. Buildings
seven stories and over would comply by May 20, 1968,
and buildings under seven stories by May 20, 1969.
Thus, the whole conversion would take place during
a two-year period. Councilman Low introduced this
amendment because he felt that the corporation
counsel's interpretation of Local Law 14 produced
too heavy a burden on the Department of Sanitation's
refuse handling capability. This "dirty streets"
argument won at least initial support from Citizens
for Clean Air, which thought that the Department of
Sanitation was overburdened and that the amendment
was easy to enforce. Radio station WINS gave similar support to Councilman Low in editorials over the
air, arguing that clean streets were a necessity
and that the Department of Sanitation could not handle increased refuse loads. Representatives of the
incinerator industry formed a group called the Metropolitan Institute for Clean Air (MICA) and also
came out for Councilman Low's amendment. They were
confident that, although the bill mandated a choice
between incineration and compaction, most building
owners would be more certain of the potential of
incineration than switching to a new form of waste
disposal about which relatively little was known.

FIGURE I

Range of Monthly Costs for Complying with On-Site Incinerator Air Pollution Control Requirements, 1968, New York City

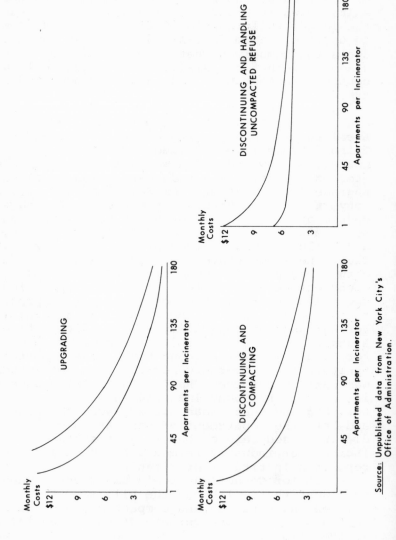

Source: Unpublished data from New York City's Office of Administration.

148

The other proposed amendment, Intro 493, was
introduced later by the city administration and would
give the operators of on-site refuse burning equipment an option to upgrade the installation, install
refuse compaction equipment in place of upgrading,
or discontinue refuse burning and place the loose
refuse for collection by the Department of Sanitation. The choice would be left to the owner, but
it was stated that the owner's response could be anticipated in some detail based on the task force
study. The amendment included a compliance timetable
of May 20, 1968, for apartment buildings with 100
or more units and buildings with 20 or less units;
May 20, 1969, for buildings with 61-99 units; and
May 20, 1970, for buildings with 21-60 units per
incinerator. This timetable was proposed because
it would enable the Department of Sanitation both
to phase in the anticipated additional refuse load
of 1,000 tons per day in incremental amounts and to
gain experience with compaction during a period when
presumably a small number of apartment houses would
be taking this option.[36] As noted earlier, the
21-60 units group would most likely prefer compaction.

The basic philosophy of the administration proposal was that on-site incineration is an inherently
inefficient method of refuse handling in that incinerators are not a piece of automatic equipment and
require continual maintenance; experience has shown
that building owners will not operate and maintain
them adequately. Note was also made of the fact
that smaller buildings are low points of emissions,
resulting in poor dispersal of pollutants in the air.
It was also argued that in most of these smaller
buildings the $6,000 to $10,000 upgrading is an
economically infeasible burden to be shared by a
small number of tenants and that the owners of these
buildings are typically in a marginal financial position and therefore most resistant to upgrading
efforts, saddling the Department of Air Pollution
Control with an enormous enforcement operation and
the concomitant delays of legal proceedings.

Comparative analysis of city-wide particulate
emissions during any time period was also said to
be misleading since multiple dwellings are concentrated in densely populated sections of the city.
Thus, particulate emissions from incinerators result
in poorer air quality where most people live than

would be suggested by city-wide ambient air readings. Furthermore, emphasis was given to the fact that on-site incineration is not a continuous operation with a steady emission rate, but is a batch operation usually conducted about four times daily, each burn taking about half an hour. During the actual burn, the particulate emission rate from a specific incinerator could approach ten times the average annual particulate emission rate.

It was pointed out by the Department of Air Pollution Control that conversion to compaction does not eliminate these arguments for it also involves considerable expense--approximately $5,000 to $6,000--for the landlord. Moreover, whereas compaction would probably cost less than upgrading, it was expected that those landlords who would stop on-site incineration under the city plan would choose compaction if they had to comply with Intro 470. This compacted material, it was argued, would add to the Department of Sanitation's burden in a shorter period of time than the incremental schedule of Intro 493. Additional criticisms raised concerning Intro 470 were that its target dates of 1968 and 1969 were "unrealistic," that the alternative of compaction would not significantly reduce the Department of Sanitation's refuse pickup load since the bulk of the refuse would be reduced but not the total tonnage, and that it was twice as expensive as the administration proposal. Both proposals could achieve the desired reduction in particulate emissions, but the cost in the private sector (excluding the New York City Housing Authority) for Intro 470 would be an estimated $36 million versus $18 million for Intro 493.

One of the big problems with Local Law 14 was that no legal action could be taken against incinerator owners prior to the day the upgrading or other act of compliance was to be completed. The Commissioner of Air Pollution Control, in testimony before the City Council in support of Intro 493, noted that:

> We have learned that we cannot clean
> the air by writing a law with unreal-
> istic deadlines. We have learned
> that we cannot enforce deadlines that
> give no lead time. We must have a
> requirement to submit applications
> at least six months prior to the
> actual date of compliance.[37]

He concluded his argument by stating:

> We cannot clean the air by locking
> ourselves into compaction--a situa-
> tion with many unknowns on the one
> hand and incineration--a perpetua-
> tion of an unwise decision on the
> other. We must allow the flexibil-
> ity for each landlord to choose the
> means best for him to meet our stan-
> dards of emission.38

The Commissioner added that the phasing out of
on-site incinerators is a part of the Department's
long-term systems approach to air pollution produced
by the burning of solid wastes. This approach was
defined as the upgrading and discontinuance of apartment house incinerators, the upgrading of existing
municipal incinerators, and the possible construction of pollution-free energy conversion incinerators that burn refuse to generate electricity.*

The proposed two amendments generated a heated
dispute in the City Council with sides being taken
on the basis of personal loyalty rather than party
affiliation. Most councilmen favored Councilman
Low's proposed amendment even though a minority report was issued by the Buildings Committee favoring
the administration proposal. The minority report
emphasized that the savings in the long run with the
use of refuse as a fuel in a total energy system
would be much greater than the short-term economies
realized from compaction or incinerator upgrading.
More to the point, the report argued that the cost
of upgrading existing incinerators could not be
properly estimated. A new installation may require
a capital cost of approximately $8,000, but revamping
an existing installation might double or triple that
price due to problems inherent in reconstructing an
old building. But, for the sake of discussion, it
was pointed out that if 7,500 apartment house incinerators were upgraded at a minimum cost of $8,000
per unit the capital cost would be $60 million and

---

*In previous testimony, mention was made of the
fact that ordinary city garbage has a heating value
that is almost 70 per cent of the equivalent heating
value per pound of coal, that is, 8,000 BTU's per
pound for garbage versus 12,000 BTU's per pound for
coal.

if another 4,500 were converted to compaction at a
minimum cost of $5,000 per unit the capital cost
would be $38 million. Thus, the total capacity in-
vestment by landlords under Intro 470 would come
to a minimum of $98 million. In addition, a mini-
mum average operating cost of $2,500 per unit for
either system would impose an annual operating cost
of $38 million. Thus, the minority report argued
that if the option of shutting down was not allowed
the capital cost to landlords would be $98 million
with $38 million in annual operating costs, with
no assurance that the systems would work. These
capital and operating costs would either be passed
on to tenants or would result in a loss of revenue
to the city because tax abatement would be necessary
in rent-controlled apartments. In either case, it
was argued that Intro 470 was an expensive proposi-
tion for the city.

The real-estate interests supported the city
administration amendment because it gave them the
options to shut down and make a choice on an economic basis. Citizens for Clean Air, who generally
felt that the air should be cleaned as soon as possible and that the cost of any such program would
be less than the cost of dirty air, changed positions during the debate. They had formerly supported the Low amendment because they did not
believe the Department of Sanitation could handle
the refuse load caused by incinerator discontinuance
but altered their view when they were persuaded that
the compaction option under Intro 470 would actually
create a greater burden for Sanitation. Because
they had changed positions, their arguments were
used by both sides in the council debate. In general, foes of the administration proposal said they
were for clean air but they did not want it at the
expense of dirty streets and were therefore protecting the Department of Sanitation.

On the eve of the voting for Intro 470, council
members were finally convinced by the Commissioner
of Air Pollution Control that Intro 470 would be
just another unenforceable law in that too many
landlords would opt for the compaction alternative--
about which relatively little was known--resulting
in too large a load for the Department of Sanitation. The amendment was sent back to committee for
the fourth time, and a compromise bill was worked
out that retained the form of Councilman Low's

amendment but somewhat more of the substance of the administration's proposal. Although neither the universal option to shut down nor the 60-unit cut-off for the lower limit of required incineration which the city administration also favored were included in the compromise version, there was an option for apartments with 40 units or less to shut down if they so desired. Two other features borrowed from Intro 493 were the three-year timetable for compliance and the requirement that an application be filed six months before an action is taken to comply with the law.

According to the compromise version, landlords with incinerators serving 20 or fewer dwelling units and those serving 100 or more units would have until July 20, 1968, to file applications describing how they would comply with the new law. They would have until December 20, 1968, to complete these installations. Those with incinerators serving 60-100 units would have to file applications before February 20, 1969, and install by October 20, 1969. The 20-60 group would have until November 20, 1969, to file and until May 20, 1970, to complete installations. In actual practice, this version would require 80 per cent of the landlords in the city either to upgrade their incinerators or install refuse-compacting equipment. The remaining 20 per cent would be allowed to shut down their incinerators and have their refuse picked up by the Department of Sanitation. If all the landlords in the latter group chose to shut down, the Sanitation Department estimated this would add about 240 tons of refuse to the daily collection total of about 10,000 tons. Even this figure would be high because air pollution and sanitation officials estimated that many of those who had the pickup option would not exercise it but would upgrade or install compacting equipment instead due to the higher cost of the former.

During the time this compromise was being worked out between the City Council and the city administration, the second interstate air pollution abatement conference was being held in New York City. At this January, 1968, conference a federal report was released that estimated that 231,000 tons of particulate matter were released into the air over the New York metropolitan area each year and stated that compliance to date with New York City's limits on refuse incineration had been only minimal.[39] New

York State Representative William Ryan attacked
Mayor Lindsay's administration as the worst polluter
of the city's air and charged that the city had
demonstrated in the last year "the worst administration of air pollution control efforts of any major
city in America."40   Similar criticism was voiced by
a representative of Citizens for Clean Air who also
charged that the Mayor had not allocated money for
aid pollution abatement to city departments. He
was quick to add, however, that his complaints were
aimed not at the Department of Air Pollution Control
but at the Lindsay Administration.

     Just before the compromise bill came up for a
vote in the council, a group known as the Metropolitan Engineers Council on Air Resources (MECAR)
passed a resolution opposing the bill. This non-
partisan organization of seven engineering groups
proposed that the City guarantee landlords permission to operate upgraded apartment house incinerators for 10 years to allay fears that incinerators
may be banned but, more importantly, took the position that it would be desirable to require the
$1,500 "incinerator package" of the over-fired air,
the gas supplemental fuel, and instrumentation,
which would remove about 75 per cent of the particulate matter from emissions, but not the $5,000
scrubber which would provide 90 per cent removal of
particulates. They believed that the state of the
art was not advanced enough to specify the type of
scrubber needed and that more research was needed
before mandating them for installation due to the
financial hardship on many building owners. They
proposed that such research and testing be carried
out over the next year and a half. The real-estate
interests grabbed the MECAR statement as a position
they would support because the capital costs were
lower and they were sure the equipment would work
effectively. The Department of Air Pollution Control, however, thought this was a very irresponsible
statement in view of the fact that by the time over
300 installations of scrubbers had been made and
10 different manufacturers of scrubbers had had
their products tested and approved by the City.

     The MECAR position statement, possibly because
it came so late in the process of making a decision
on the amendment to Local Law 14, had little impact
on the people supporting the compromise bill, and
the revision to the law was passed by the City

Council and signed by the Mayor in March, 1968.
The revision of Local Law 14 made city officials
fairly confident that air pollution from on-site
incinerators would finally be dealt with effectively. Due to the magnitude of the conversion work
needed, the Department of Air Pollution Control
thought it unlikely that all installations would be
completed by the required deadlines but that on the
whole compliance would be good with little conscious
evasion of the requirements by building owners. The
only question of concern was the response of the
compactor industry which at that time had not come
forward to have their compactors tested by the City.
In a sense, it was the same development as occurred
in the case of getting the incinerator manufacturers
and installers alerted to the opportunities available in the city. Initial experience suggested
that building owners liked them because their use
reduces the number of cans that have to stand out
in front of the building and there are not so many
cans to carry in and out. The City found that use
of compactor equipment affects the refuse collection
cost structure of about $25.00 a ton very little
because the collection trucks compact to about the
same degree.

A year later (March, 1969) found the on-site
incinerator provisions of Local Law 14 still a center
of controversy. A lawsuit filed by two landlords
contended that Local Law 14 was unconstitutional.
A State Supreme Court judge enjoined the City from
invoking the penalties of the law against the landlords until a trial could be held to determine
whether the compliance timetable and penalties were
"unconstitutionally oppressive."[41] Given the uncertainty associated with the unresolved lawsuit,
other landlords were reticent to sign a contract
for the installation of upgrading or compaction
equipment. Compliance with the revised law was
thus still less than complete.

Thus, by the end of March, 1969, three months
after the deadline for upgrading or closing the
first group of about 3,000 incinerators, only 375
units had been improved and certified for operation
and only 44 compactors had been installed. Applications for discontinuance had been filed for 1,068
units. No units have been sealed, although the law
provides for such action. The Department of Air
Pollution Control was avoiding court procedures to

compliance wherever possible if the land-
re taking some action. In the second phase,
g about 5,000 units, 217 had been upgraded,
ions had been approved for 352 more, and
lords had opted for compactors. Only 168
al applications had been filed.

Continuing problems were the inability of the
Department of Sanitation to remove large amounts of
additional refuse that resulted when incinerators
were shut down and the difficulty of landlords in
getting contractors to do upgrading work. The latter
problem was reinforced by the fact that most landlords waited until just before the deadline before
taking any action, thereby swamping the contractors
with orders.

Problems were still in evidence in other areas
of air pollution abatement in the city that could
affect the response to this aspect of Local Law 14.
In the time since the law was passed, sulfur dioxide
emissions in the city were reduced by 25 per cent.
But this had been accomplished entirely through the
efforts of Consolidated Edison by its switch to low-
sulfur oil. The city had not "cleaned its own
house." In pollution abatement programs where governmental initiative is required, little progress
had been made due to the failure of the City to
budget the necessary funds, and, as a result, the
upgrading of municipal incinerators was considerably
behind schedule. May, 1969, also saw the announce-
ment that due to the lack of funds the incinerators
in the apartment houses operated by the Housing
Authority would not be required to comply with Local
Law 14 for the forseeable future. Because of this
lack of municipal leadership, it is difficult to
anticipate when the on-site incinerator problem
will finally be resolved.

THE NEW YORK EXPERIENCE REVIEWED

Comparison with Los Angeles

The air pollution problems in Los Angeles and
New York City are in some senses fundamentally different. A large percentage of the pollution in Los
Angeles is currently caused by automobile emissions
whereas New York is still faced with controlling

contaminants from stationary sources. New York only
occasionally has the severely restricted mixing
height overhead that is common in Los Angeles but
suffers from a much higher sulfur dioxide and particulate content in the air caused by incineration
and the burning of fuel oil in electricity generation and heating plants. Consolidated Edison, the
major public utility in New York City, has in the
last year and a half reduced its emissions of sulfur
dioxide considerably by switching to low-sulfur
fuel oil, whereas Southern California Edison and
the Los Angeles Department of Water and Power rely
on natural gas for electricity generation for about
ten months of the year, with low-sulfur oil being
used for only about two months. New York City's
sputtering attack on municipal and on-site incineration has yet to yield significant results. No
attempt has been made by the City to control automobile emissions.

Both control agencies rely on similar types of
rules and regulations and the use of permits and
have operated in a crisis environment in which there
has been strong public support for air pollution
abatement. But the sense of crisis and public support have probably been greater in the Los Angeles
region. The stinging of the eyes and the severe
restriction of visibility associated with the Los
Angeles smog brought home clearly to Los Angeles
residents the need to reduce pollution emissions.
The public health arguments of the Los Angeles
Air Pollution Control District only reinforced this
perceived need. New Yorkers, beset also by other
problems such as soaring welfare and medical costs,
school decentralization, transportation congestion,
and racial fears, have not focused their concern
about air pollution to the extent that Los Angeles
residents have. It can also be argued that both
the public statements concerning the negative health
effects of air pollution in New York City by city
air pollution officials and the U.S. Public Health
Service representatives and the visible accumulation
of dirt resulting from particulate fallout had a
lesser impact on New Yorkers than the eye-stinging
smog of Los Angeles had on its residents.

Air pollution in New York City has been defined
as a "people-oriented" problem in that industrial
emissions are of minor importance.[42] Local Law 14
therefore focused on the disposal of refuse by

burning and the emission of pollutants during the process of burning fuel for space heating and electricity generation. After some early opposition in 1966 to proposed regulations, Con Ed has been very cooperative in abating its sulfur dioxide emissions and is continually praised by the Department of Air Pollution Control for its efforts. The law mandated the use of low-sulfur fuel oil according to a time schedule that incrementally reduced the sulfur content of the oil. Due in part to the availability of low-sulfur oil from recently developed oil fields in Latin America, Con Ed was able to meet the deadlines of Local Law 14 ahead of schedule. The problems with the law, in the final analysis, focus on the city administration itself and the owners of thousands of apartment house incinerators. Difficulties have stemmed from a poorly written law, a lack of foresight by the originators of the law, disagreements within the city administration, unforeseen enforcement problems, a legal suit, an amendment process (of Local Law 14) with political overtones, and a belated introduction of economic analysis of the issue. Related to the on-site incinerator issue is the requirement in Local Law 14 that municipal incinerators be upgraded or shut down according to a specified schedule. Due to the lack of available municipal funds and, secondarily, to inadequate time to order, install, and "de-bug" control equipment, the City could not comply with the law's requirements affecting municipal incinerators.

The Actors Involved

This study of air pollution control in New York City has concentrated on activities from 1965 onward, as 1965 was about the time that air pollution became a significant public issue in the city. The issue arose partly as a result of both internal and external pressures. The external pressures were exerted on the city government by the U.S. Department of Health, Education and Welfare and the New York State government, both of which believed that a serious air pollution problem existed in the city and that the city government was giving inadequate attention to it. Within the city, officials responded principally to the active campaign of Citizens for Clean Air but also to a general concern for cleaner air by New York City residents. In addition

to the Department of Air Pollution Control, the
principal actors involved in the decision-making
process related to the on-site incinerator aspects
of Local Law 14 can be listed, more or less in the
order in which they became involved, as follows:

(1) U.S. Department of Health, Education and
    Welfare

(2) Councilman Robert Low and the City Council

(3) Citizens for Clean Air

(4) Mayor Lindsay and the Office of Administra-
    tion

(5) Other city departments and the corporation
    counsel

(6) The New York State Air Pollution Control
    Board

(7) The New York City Real Estate Board (Rep-
    resenting the apartment house owners)

(8) The New York Business Council for Clean Air

(9) The Department of Sanitation

(10) Metropolitan Engineers Council for Air
     Resources (MECAR)

The most important participants, however, were the
City Council, the Mayor and the Department of Air
Pollution Control, the Department of Sanitation,
and, as a group, the thousands of apartment house
owners.

The Major Issues

In retrospect, the major concerns that were in
the minds of decision-makers who influenced, or attempted to influence, the formulation of the on-site
incineration aspects of Local Law 14 were solid
waste disposal, refuse transport, the assignment of
abatement costs, and various questions related to
uncertainty.

Solid Waste Disposal

Unlike Los Angeles, New York City is severely
restricted in terms of area available for solid
waste disposal. Most of the areas serving as a re-
pository for landfill materials over the past 20
years or more have been "wetlands" or marine estu-
aries. These have been sharply reduced since 1900,
and it has been projected that presently designated

sites could be exhausted in 1974.[43] The past
effectiveness of solid waste disposal has been at
the expense of the natural ecology of these areas.

The output of solid wastes in New York City is
increasing 3 per cent annually. At this rate, it
is expected that the per capita generation of waste
will increase from the current 4.5 pounds to 6
pounds in 1978, resulting in an additional one million tons of refuse. In the city, 79 per cent of
all refuse is burnable. If the original on-site
incinerator upgrading provisions of Local Law 14
had been fully enforced, about 75,000 tons of landfill (incinerator residue) per year would have been
produced. At the other extreme, shutting down all
the on-site incinerators and the municipal incinerators in the city would mean an additional 750,000
tons per year of landfill in the form of "raw refuse." The City Council, in mandating incinerator
upgrading, had these facts squarely in mind.

Refuse Transport

Closely associated with the landfill issue was
the "dirty streets" argument. If refuse was not
going to be incinerated at the site where it was
produced, it would have to be transported to the
street in cans where it would await pickup by Department of Sanitation trucks and thence be taken
either to a municipal incinerator or landfill site.
Proponents of on-site incinerator upgrading rightly
pointed out that the city's streets were not particularly clean and shutting down incinerators with
the resultant need for refuse removal by truck would
add to the problem. This situation was aggravated
by a series of personal disagreements between the
Mayor and the Commissioner of Sanitation. (The
Commissioner was eventually relieved of his duties
by the Mayor.) As noted earlier, the Commissioner
made a series of public statements criticizing the
on-site incinerator aspects of Local Law 14. Although a number of these can be viewed as ploys in
a personal conflict with the Mayor, certain of his
points are pertinent to the issue. Particularly
important was the fact that the Department of Sanitation had inadequate time to prepare for the handling of an increased but unknown quantity of refuse.
Partially because of a lack of foresight on the part
of the City Council, partially due to a lack of a
conscientious effort by the Department of Sanitation
in preparing to pick up the refuse, and later, due

to a failure of the City to appropriate sufficient
funds soon enough to buy needed garbage trucks,
the City did not have the capacity to remove a large
amount of additional refuse in May, 1968. In 1969,
due to a continuing municipal financial crisis that
restricted the size of the Department of Sanitation's
budget, the streets were acknowledged by city officials to be dirtier than during previous years.

The Assignment of Abatement Costs

In Local Law 14, emission of pollutants in
the air is defined as a public nuisance.[44] Thus,
specific polluters are responsible for controlling
their emissions. In the original on-site incinerator provisions of the law, the benefits accrued
to the general public whereas the costs of abatement fell entirely on the apartment house owners.
As noted, these costs were capricious in their distribution, particularly those that would have fallen
on the owner of a small apartment building.

In the year before the law was passed, there was
much talk of "cleaning up the air at any cost." But
during this period, New York City realized that it
was in a fiscal crisis with revenues down and demands
for expenditures up. Therefore, the City Council
looked for economical solutions to the air pollution problem--economical in the sense of requiring
a small amount of city funds. Considering total
public and private abatement costs, a less expensive approach to abatement in the long run would
have been to shut down all on-site incinerators
completely and have the Department of Sanitation
transport the refuse to municipal incinerators or
landfill sites.* However, this approach would have
involved significantly greater costs to the city
and an almost proportionate reduction in the out-of-
pocket costs to the landlord (the polluter).

New York City budget officials and engineers
tend to make decisions involving the expenditure of
public funds after "living with the issue" for some

---

*Considerations associated with nonquantifiable
costs such as the reduction of wetlands by landfill
and aesthetics and noise related to removal of refuse from buildings are not considered in this less
expensive approach.

time, with considerable emphasis given to spreading
out the costs to the city over a "reasonable period
of time."[45] In a majority of cases, city budget
officials tend to make decisions with more emphasis
on the cost of implementation than on the benefits
accruing from some action. Thus, although suppor-
ters of air pollution control such as Citizens for
Clean Air were calling for the reduction of air
pollution regardless of cost, city budget officials
first narrowly viewed the problem as one of minimizing the cost to the city almost regardless of the
amount of pollution that would be abated.[46]

Dealing with Uncertainty

Unlike the Los Angeles situation, there has been
much less uncertainty about the sources of air pollution in New York City. There was a considerable
degree of consensus that refuse and fuel oil combustion were major villains. Uncertainties that
did exist were of a technological, logistical,
human, and legal nature. Examples include:

(1) Technological--Would wet scrubbers operate
    efficiently on incinerator stacks?
(2) Logistical--Would contractors be available
    to do the upgrading work?
(3) Human--How would apartment house owners
    behave when given a free choice of options
    for dealing with their pollution emissions?
(4) Legal--Would the legal suit result in a
    showing of inequity in Local Law 14?

The only effective response to these types of uncertainty by city officials, although belated, was
the study dealing with the costs associated with the
three alternatives to uncontrolled incineration.

The Consideration of Alternatives

The only alternatives given serious consideration for dealing with the on-site incinerator problem were the following: upgrading with a scrubber,
upgrading except for a scrubber, shutting down and
compacting refuse, and shutting down without compacting. However, these were not viable alternatives open to the technical staff of the Department
of Air Pollution Control. Rather than specifying
objectives in terms of air quality, Local Law 14

specified the detailed process by which emissions
were to be abated. No flexibility was provided.
Mayor Lindsay's early position that installation of
proper monitoring devices for the continuous recording of emissions from smokestacks which would make
it unnecessary to specify the kind of control equipment to keep the emissions within any prescribed
limit was never given serious consideration. The
suggestion that abatement equipment design standards,
which specified a 90 per cent reduction of emissions,
be lowered for smaller buildings was also not given
much consideration. A variant of this last suggestion was the MECAR proposal that appeared late in
the deliberations on the revision of Local Law 14.
MECAR's proposal for requiring the $1,500 "incin-
erator package," which would result in an estimated
75 per cent reduction in pollutant emissions, but
not the $5,000 scrubber, which was said to be im-
perfectly developed, also did not receive much consideration due to the timing of its introduction.

Municipal Leadership and Political Objectives

During the hearings on Local Law 14, it was
stated time and again by representatives of apartment house owners that private citizens should not
be required to upgrade their incinerators before
the city "cleaned its own house." This, of course,
referred to the upgrading of incinerators in city-
owned buildings such as those of the Housing Authority and the upgrading of the large municipal
incinerators. Although such upgrading was written
into Local Law 14 so that it would take place concurrent with the upgrading of private incinerators,
compliance was little better than in the private
sector. Due to the magnitude of both tasks, and the
lack of adequate time for budgeting, signing contracts, and getting the actual work done, very few
on-site incinerators owned by the city were actually
upgraded by the May, 1967, deadline. The complexity
of the task can be indicated by the job facing the
Housing Authority. It had to upgrade 2,745 on-site
incinerators at a cost of $17 million, but by June,
1967, although contracts for the work had been
signed, actual upgrading was completed or under way
on only 400. In mid-1969, the upgrading of Housing
Authority incinerators was suspended due to lack
of funds. In like manner, the large municipal

incinerators were not upgraded by the May, 1969,
deadline due to inadequate funding (preventing the
signing of contracts) and insufficient time for
installation and "de-bugging" of electrostatic
precipitators and scrubbers. This lack of municipal
leadership undoubtedly hampered the efforts of the
Department of Air Pollution Control to require private citizens to upgrade.

Due to these delays "politically acceptable"
dates for showing tangible results in the city's
pollution abatement program also could not be met.
Mayor Lindsay's administration entered office with
the new Local Law 14 almost in hand. Because he
had campaigned on a clean air platform, Mayor
Lindsay naturally wanted to markedly reduce air
pollution in New York City during his term in office.
(This consideration also applied to the City Council.) But by the time of the next city elections,
the municipal incinerators that were not obsolete
and therefore scheduled to be shut down were not
yet completely upgraded. Mayor Lindsay's campaign
commitment for clean air is a partial explanation
for the unrealistic deadline adopted for installation of pollution control equipment. More generally,
the public desire for cleaner air contributed to a
lack of foresight by legislators concerning practical problems involved in implementing Local Law 14.
This myopia produced disagreements among city departments, a legal suit, a necessary amendment to
the law, and considerable adverse publicity for the
city administration.

Time and Technology

New regulations, such as those relating to air
pollution control, often require new responses from
those parties identified as polluters. Typically,
this group has to respond according to a set time
schedule. In New York City, there were considerable
complaints by apartment house owners that there was
inadequate time allowance to complete the required
abatement. This complaint is a very common one,
but in this case it seemed to possess some validity.
Due to the large number of conversions and upgrad-
ings that would need to be completed, it was soon
obvious to both polluter and controller that the
set deadlines could not be met. The time constraint

problem was compounded by questions concerning the efficiency of the mandated control equipment and the lack of authority on the part of the Commissioner of Air Pollution Control to require some degree of compliance with Local Law 14 before the deadline of May 20, 1967.

The Role of Bargaining Behavior

New York City has suffered through a large number of strikes of various sorts during the late 1960's. More often than not, confrontation rather than negotiation has been used to bring issues to a head. In like manner, the formulators of the on-site incinerator aspects of Local Law 14 seemingly adopted an intractable attitude when presented with the law's suggested shortcomings. Somewhat surprisingly, the compromise that took place was not between the polluter and the regulator, but between different parts of the city government--the City Council and the City administration. In a more general sense, the characteristics of bargaining behavior reviewed in Chapter 3 were seldom seen.

In sum, the on-site incinerator control program cannot be considered a successful one. As outlined, the reasons for the failure are many. Progress is severely behind the schedule outlined in the revised law. A more pragmatic approach to this one type of air quality management would have seemingly yielded better results. Suggestions for such an approach utilizing bargaining behavior are outlined in the following chapter.

NOTES

1. New York Sanitary Code (1948), Sections 211-12. The smoke control unit was abolished in an economy move in 1934.

2. See Local Law 5 (1949); Local Laws 114, 115 (1952). For licensing power, see Local Law 115, Section 892-4.0.

3. The legal basis for the city's control program is contained in Chapter 41 of the City Charter, Chapter 41 of The Administrative Code, and the rules and regulations of the Department of Air Pollution Control.

4. Minutes of the Council, June 22, 1965, pp. 1186-1258. Councilman Low was also the first chairman for Citizens for Clean Air.

5. Ibid., p. 1190.

6. Freedom to Breathe, Report of the Mayor's Task Force on Air Pollution in the City of New York, June 20, 1966.

7. New York Times, March 26, 1966.

8. Ibid.

9. Ibid.

10. Local Law 14 (1966); New York Times, May 24, 1966.

11. See "Switching to Low Sulfur Oil: Con Ed's Story," Environmental Science and Technology, III (December, 1968), 1072-73.

12. Local Law 14, May 20, 1966, New York City Administrative Code 892-4.3.

13. Ibid., 893-3.0.

14. See "Air Pollution in New York City," Report of the Special Committee to Investigate Air Pollution of the New York City Council, Minutes of the City Council, June 22, 1965, pp. 1227-28.

15. New York Times, December 10, 1966.

16. "Criteria Used for Upgrading Existing Apartment House Incinerators in the City of New York," Department of Air Pollution Control, January, 1967.

17. Mayor's Office of Administration, New York City, Report of Task Force No. 1 of the Committee on Implementation of Local Law 14, November 28, 1966. (Mimeographed.)

18. Ibid., pp. 3-4

19. Ibid., p. 6.

20. H. Denny and E. Limoges, "Summary of Our Memorandum--Public Law 14; Estimate of Impact Regarding Requiring Upgrading vs. Abandonment of Apartment House Incinerators," New York City Department of City Planning, December, 1966, p. 3.

21. U.S. Public Health Service, "Summary of Conference and Conclusions and Recommendations on Interstate Air Pollution--New York-New Jersey Metropolitan Area," January, 1967, p. 13.

22. Ibid., p. 15.

23. New York Times, April 25, 1967.

24. Ibid. The same article carried the seemingly contradictory statement that, although there were 9,000 incinerators that needed to be upgraded, only 600 letters had been received from landlords by the Department of Air Pollution Control indicating an intention to comply with the law.

25. Ibid. Although New York State laws provide for fines up to $1,000 for persons violating public health laws concerning air pollution, with a $200 fine for each day the violation continues, the lesser fine schedule was adopted.

26. The City finally decided to charge $0.55 for collecting a cubic yard of loose garbage and $1.10 for bundled garbage. New York Times, May 15, 1967.

27. New York Times, May 1, 1967.

28. New York Times, May 12, 1967.

29. New York Times, May 16, 1967.

30. New York Times, May 23, 1967.

31. New York Times, April 25, 1967.

32. Austin Heller, "Status Report on the On-Site Incinerator Program," New York City Department of Air Pollution Control, July 31, 1967, p. 2.

33. McKinsey & Company, "Issue Mapping" and "Refuse Disposal Issue Map," August, 1967.

34.   "Economics of Upgrading or Discontinuing Incineration," Mayor's Office of Administration, New York City, October 3, 1967, p. 2. (Mimeographed.)

35.   Ibid., p. 6.

36.   Unpublished testimony of Commissioner Austin Heller, November 13, 1967.

37.   Ibid.

38.   Ibid.

39.   New York Times, January 29, 1968.

40.   New York Times, January 31, 1968.

41.   New York Times, March 30, 1969.

42.   Interview with Mrs. B. Brand Konheim, Director, Public Information and Education, New York City Department of Air Pollution Control.

43.   S. Marlow, "On-Site Incineration--The View of the Regulatory Air Pollution Control Agency" (Paper presented before the New York City Department of Air Pollution Control Refuse Disposal Workshop, December 9, 1967), Freedom to Breathe, op. cit., pp. 49-54.

44.   Section 892-1.0.

45.   Interview with Stanley Penil and Murray Herman, Mayor's Office of Administration, August, 1968.

46.   Ibid.

PART **III**

PLANNING FOR THE FUTURE

CHAPTER **7** A BARGAINING
BEHAVIOR
FRAMEWORK

The Los Angeles experience outlined in this
study, and to a lesser extent the New York City
experience, cannot be taken as representative of
what future efforts at air pollution control might
be like because the decision environment has changed
with the passage of time. More is known about the
uncertainties concerning the effects of air pollution, the means of controlling it, and the technology to do the job. Federal support and research,
represented only in part by the development of air
quality criteria by the Department of Health, Education and Welfare, will enable control agencies
to reduce the number of uncertainties with which
they have to deal. Lessons can be learned from
examining the experience to date, however; the basic
nature of the problem will not change. This chapter,
then, is an attempt to extract from the Los Angeles
and New York City experiences some generalizations
that bear upon current and future planning and
decision-making for air quality management. These
generalizations lead to suggestions for structuring
air quality management programs required under the
Air Quality Act of 1967.

The chapter is divided into four parts. The
first deals with the role of the rational model and
bargaining in air quality management. The second
translates the material covered in this volume into
a proposal for managing air quality. The third dis-
cusses the political and institutional structure
within which decisions are going to have to be made.
Finally, the concluding section tries to put the
decision-making problem in perspective.

THE ROLE OF THE
RATIONAL MODEL AND BARGAINING

The key issues discussed include the following.
What is the role of the rational model in air quality management in terms of setting objectives,
criteria, and standards and evaluating experience?
Can a least-cost solution be identified? Can it be
achieved in the given political and institutional
framework? Can the various types of uncertainties
in air quality management be clearly specified and
dealt with effectively? Does bargaining exist in
air quality management? If it does, is its role
positive or negative? If it does, what are its
characteristics? Can bargaining behavior be effectively separated from bargaining outcomes, i.e.,
compromises, and utilized to approach least-cost
solutions?

The Los Angeles Experience

Air pollution control in Los Angeles was a
pioneering effort where some degree of trial and
error was a costly necessity.* The full flavor of
the rational model, with its considerable information requirements, could not have been fully applied
during the first decade of the existence of the Los
Angeles Air Pollution Control District due to the
sheer lack of knowledge with which the agency had
to deal. Los Angeles air pollution control officials readily point out that in retrospect their
efforts might not necessarily have been optimal or
resulting in a minimum-cost solution but add that
in the light of the then existing knowledge, their
activities were logical and sound. This statement
takes on added meaning when the obvious severity of
the problem is considered together with the strong
public mandate in the Los Angeles Basin to control
the smog.

---

*At one point in the control program, a $1
million precipitator was installed on one of the
electricity generating plants in the Los Angeles
area. It never worked efficiently and was eventually dismantled.

The objective of the Los Angeles program was
initially to return to the level of air quality
that existed in 1939--the last year that the air
was perceived to be "clean" in the Los Angeles
Basin. Whereas this objective could not be operationalized due to the lack of air quality measurements for that year, the District redefined its
principal objective to be the maximum possible reduction of air pollution within its jurisdiction.
It has pursued this objective with vigor with the
support of the Los Angeles County Board of Commissioners. Inasmuch as the automobile remains a
principal polluter in the Los Angeles Basin, only
incremental progress has been made toward this goal.

The major emphasis given to research on air
pollution in the laboratories of the District represents an attempt to develop viable air quality
criteria with which to support enforcement procedures. In like manner, research on abatement technology yielded indispensable information for the
evaluation of control techniques. The emphasis
placed on negative health effects of air pollution
by the Los Angeles Air Pollution Control District
when supporting proposed or existing abatement
policies can be viewed as setting a constraint that
had to be met. The District staff argued that, because of the postulated relationship between air
pollution and such health problems as respiratory
disease, ambient air pollution levels needed to be
reduced almost regardless of cost. The cost sensitivity of this constraint, however, was never made
explicit. Benefit-cost analysis was viewed by the
District as a gambit used by those being regulated
to avoid and delay the imposition of regulations
to achieve this end.

In theory, intermittent control of pollution
is more optimal in the sense of fitting into the
least-cost solution than continuous, direct regulation. But in support of such continuous regulation
the Los Angeles Air Pollution Control District
raised serious questions about the desirability of
using intermittent control methods. In response to
the Western Oil and Gas Association's request for
discontinuous control related to weather conditions,
four main objections were raised: (1) Legal suits
based on equity considerations could be filed if a
privilege of intermittent pollution emissions was
extended to one segment of industry and denied to

others. (2) It would be difficult to develop a legally enforceable notification system that would effectively and rapidly require polluters to abate emissions on an intermittent basis. (3) There could be a question of the legality of requiring shifts in fuels on the basis of weather forecasts that were not always accurate. (4) Finally, continuous stack-monitoring equipment was expensive and difficult to maintain in proper operating order and often required additional manpower to operate.

These arguments carried sufficient weight with the Los Angeles County Commissioners that to this day no form of intermittent control of stationary sources of air pollution is allowed. The only form of intermittent control that exists is the voluntary reduction by Los Angeles citizens of the number and length of automobile trips during periods of a smog alert. These voluntary reductions, requested by the District and announced over radio and television, have the objective of reducing carbon monoxide emissions into the ambient air during periods of high pollution concentrations. It is impossible to evaluate the effectiveness of this program, although the number of person trips reduced during a smog alert by this method during a typical working day is probably negligible due to the mandatory nature of most trips, i.e., home to work.

The New York City Experience

From the viewpoint of applying the rational model, the contemporary experience in New York City can be considered more open to criticism than the Los Angeles decisions, which now are in many cases from 10 to 20 years old. Whereas the on-site incinerator clause of Local Law 14 and subsequent revisions are yet to be fully carried out, the decisions made can still be considered current. The original law cited not objectives to be achieved but the nature of mandated control equipment. Ambient air quality goals were not adopted by the New York City Department of Air Pollution Control (now called the Department of Air Resources) until some time after this detailed legislation was signed into law. Flexibility was discouraged by the lack of allowance for alternative approaches to abatement, and the originators of the law gave inadequate attention to possible cost consequences of the law's requirements.

The hearings on the criteria for upgrading
on-site incinerators seemingly reflected a similar
position by New York City air pollution control
personnel to that held in Los Angeles--the objective
of maximum possible reduction of air pollution. The
90 per cent reduction in particulate emissions to
be attained by use of a scrubber increased the costs
to the apartment house owner by five times over the
75 per cent reduction attainable by using just the
"incinerator package."

Due to a financial crisis in the city, an attempt was made to minimize municipal costs rather
than total resource costs. More emphasis was also
given to spreading the costs over a considerable
period of time rather than maximizing benefits.
As in Los Angeles, direct, continuous control has
been the adopted approach to air pollution abatement. The use of low-sulfur fuels has been mandated.
In the specific case of on-site incineration, the
mandating of specific control equipment reduced to
almost zero the possibility of any flexibility in
control technique. Early in his administration,
Mayor Lindsay raised the most specific objection
to the mandated control equipment, but his request
for monitoring devices was rejected by City Council
members as "too long range" and "too vast a job."

The revisions in Local Law 14 passed over a
year after the original law's adoption showed a recognition of the need for some flexibility in control
technique. The options for shutting down, upgrading, or conversion to compaction introduced some
degree of flexibility.

The Emphasis on Costs

It is a basic supposition in planning for
environmental quality that benefits are ill defined
and that major emphasis must therefore be given to
the cost side of the equation. The two case studies
point out that costs are also often ill defined,
not only in terms of their magnitude but also in
their distribution. The New York City experience
clearly shows the difficulties that can arise when
inadequate attention is given to the implications
of assigning abatement costs to small economic units.
This problem is often overlooked when control agencies concentrate on large industrial firms, groups
of firms, or public utilities that emit pollutants.

The designation of benefits, on the other hand, receives a great deal of public discussion but is still the center of a great deal of controversy. Due to the crude nature of benefit estimation, a rigorous comparison of benefits and costs in air quality management has not been carried out to date. Research on the benefits of air pollution abatement by control agencies has been used instead to justify existing or anticipated control measures. Air pollution abatement has been approached incrementally, with villains identified, plans made to abate the source of pollution, and the magnitude of the anticipated control justified by benefit estimation. A sophisticated systems approach wherein the relationships between air quality and all the emitters of pollution are specified and considered in an air quality management program has not been attempted to date.

Air Quality Standards

The Los Angeles Air Pollution Control District, facing great uncertainty concerning the relationship between pollutant emissions and ambient air quality, placed little reliance on air quality standards. Although state standards applied in Los Angeles, they were not a prominent part of the air pollution abatement program. Due to the severity of the smog attacks, maximum abatement of all emissions was the cornerstone of abatement activities. Reflecting the development of air quality management in the United States, New York City had by late 1966 tentatively adopted regional air quality standards developed by the state. But the city's air-monitoring network was not put into operation until late 1968, so that these standards did not play a significant role in early control efforts in the city. The Department of Air Pollution Control had little basis for relating emission standards to air quality standards even two years after the passing of Local Law 14.

Dealing with Uncertainty

The specification of uncertainty is critical in a successful application of the rational decision model. Decision-making in air pollution control in the two instances had to deal with uncertainty in a

variety of forms.* Innovation in the use of effluent fees or even the use of payments and subsidies
received little attention because they had not been
proven to be reliable methods of abating pollution.
Efforts at air pollution control in the two cities,
both operating without much precedent, were based
on approaches that were thought able to yield pre-
dictable results--in some cases, almost seemingly
regardless of the abatement costs involved.

Uncertainty as to the legality of existing or
proposed regulations that are a part of air quality
management programs seems to be a continuing central issue. Associated with almost all attempts
to control air pollution from different sources has
been the final reliance by the emitters of pollution
on the courts and the legal system to make the definitive decision on the validity of air pollution
control regulations. The air pollution control
agencies have also depended on legal decisions to
consolidate their positions when there have been
uncertainties associated with jurisdictional conflicts with other governmental agencies. This leads
to the conclusion that any decision model that attempts to explain how air pollution is effectively
reduced by control agencies must consider the role
of the legal system in influencing the behavior of
both the control agency and the emitter of pollution. This point is developed further later in this
chapter.

What can be called "logistical uncertainty" is
a prominent problem. When a large number of polluters must abate their pollution, the private market
must respond by providing either services, abatement equipment, or different fuels to parties if
they are to meet pollution regulations. Major con-
troversies have arisen in both Los Angeles and New
York City relating to the availability of these inputs. It is therefore incumbent on any air quality

---

*Representative problems include inherent com-
plexities in defining air pollution and its effects,
the primitive state or absence of much required data,
some inevitable arbitrariness in the specification
of constraints, the absence of fully satisfactory
means of handling the risk inherent in natural
phenomena, and the uncertainties involved in fore-
casting future economic variables.

management agency to consider the implications of
their regulations in terms of the logistics of compliance.

Technological uncertainty is an issue often
raised by polluters when faced with regulations
requiring investment in abatement equipment. Often
this complaint is made with some justification,
but probably just as often it is not. Research on
control technology is thus a critical element in
air quality management, suggesting the need for a
large technical staff within the control agency.
Technological uncertainty means uncertain costs for
the party that has to abate its pollution. The common complaint is that regulations might require the
installation of expensive abatement equipment that
might not prove to operate effectively, necessitat-
ing the replacement or modification of such equipment at an additional cost. Whereas this point has
arisen in almost every instance of pollution abatement reviewed in this study, research on and the
detailed specification of control costs needs to
be given major emphasis in agency operations.

The Evaluation Stage

Unlike water quality management, evaluation of
experience receives major emphasis in air pollution
control because programs are less oriented to the
construction of capital intensive facilities. Air
quality management is somewhat less of a "one-shot"
operation. Solutions to water pollution problems,
such as the construction of a dam for low flow
augmentation or a municipal sewage treatment plant,
do not have their direct analogies. Air quality
management relies less on capital facilities programming and more, at least in a relative sense, on
regulations requiring pollution abatement by small
economic units. These regulations have to be justified by air pollution control authorities if the
control agency is going to continue to operate
effectively. Thus, status reports showing reduction
in air pollution are used as an indicator of agency
effectiveness and as a justification for further
control. Alternative approaches to pollution abatement to those utilized have not been evaluated because, unfortunately, they have not been tried.

The Utility of the Rational Model

Due to the informational requirements of the rational model, it has not been applied with any rigor in the two programs surveyed in this study. This situation is clearly changing at the present time, with research on air pollution carried out on many fronts. Many of the data deficiencies will become less important in the foreseeable future, suggesting new opportunities to apply the rational model in more detail. The primary result of data collection and research will be a specification of the nature of the many aspects of the uncertainty constraint--a considerable obstacle that existing control efforts have had to face. But experience to date clearly reveals that a solution that minimizes social costs is not at hand. Due to the multiple considerations outlined above, new thought needs to be given to approaches that consider all pertinent costs. The economist's least-cost solution, often presented in little more than skeletal form in theoretical discussions, is insufficient to deal with the complexities that air pollution control officials must face in the American urban environment of today. The following is presented as a suggestion for reducing some of these inevitable problems to manageable proportions.

Bargaining Behavior

Only one example of pro forma bargaining was observed in the two case studies--the compromise over the amendment to the incinerator clause of Local Law 14 between the New York City Council and the Mayor and Commissioner of Air Pollution Control. As noted earlier, minor cases of bargaining occurred in Los Angeles, but these were not considered a central part of the regulatory process. Although bargaining has existed in the air quality management experience of the two cities in a small way, there is inadequate data to reveal whether it has been a positive or negative influence. This unfortunate lack of empirical data prevents a comparison of potential least-cost solutions and bargaining solutions.

The only conclusion of some utility is arrived at by deduction rather than from the observation

of experience. As noted earlier, in game theory,
rational agreement is a psychic convergence of
expectations. In simpler terms, this means that
agreement involves the striking of balances. As
a strategist, then, the air pollution control official must initially devote considerable attention
to the formulation of the problem he is to deal
with. Using the terminology reviewed earlier, his
strategy should be to define the bargaining range,
the boundary of possibility, and possibly even the
contact points so that the bargaining game will be
formulated in such a manner that his minimum dis-
position and that of the emitter of pollution are
not extremely different. To continue the terminology reviewed in Chapter 3, this would result in
the development of a number of overlapping acceptable sets--positions where agreement can be reached
without major compromises.

An example from the water resource field illustrates one possible approach. Currently, water
quality standards are set after a range of alternatives are developed and subjected to review by
the public and interested parties. Examples to date
suggest that a standard in the middle of the range
from the status quo to a high degree of treatment
at a high cost tends to be picked. (Examples are the
water quality standards for the Delaware Basin and
the State of North Carolina.)[1] With this knowledge
in mind, alternatives could be so formulated that
the alternative preferred by the pollution agency
could be placed in this favorable position.

The useful conclusions that result from the
case studies suggest that tangible benefits can be
realized by understanding and utilizing the responses
broadly defined as bargaining behavior in Chapter 3.
Such behavior is useful as a procedure for conflict
avoidance and resolution. The studies explicitly
and implicitly reveal that a knowledge of bargaining
behavior on the part of air pollution control personnel would yield tangible rewards. Four of the
more obvious resulting benefits would be (a) a reduction in the psychological opposition to regulation, (b) an improvement of communication between
the emitter of pollution and the control agency,
(c) open consideration of unforeseen costs, and
(d) specification of the uncertainty constraint.
How these benefits could be achieved in part by
agency organizational design is treated in some
detail in a following section of this chapter.

AN AIR QUALITY MANAGEMENT PROPOSAL

Effective Management
and Bargaining Behavior

Experience dictates that the achievement of
effective air pollution control should be viewed
as a pragmatic strategy involving a series of dis-
crete phases in which the least-cost solution is
not defined in detail.   Rather, a search is made
that is in effect a form of incremental cost-effectiveness analysis.   Initial activity on the part
of the control agency should make it clear to the
sponsoring legislative body or bodies that one of
its first responsibilities is to clean their own
houses by, for example, upgrading or abandoning
any governmentally owned incinerators and reducing
the emission levels from governmental heating and
electricity generating plants.   This is necessary
to avoid the embarrassing--and legitimate--charge
that a governmental jurisdiction is forcing the
private sector to clean up its pollution while continuing to pollute the air itself.   This has been
a continuing accusation in New York City, where the
municipal incinerators had not been upgraded by
the time private on-site incinerators were to be
upgraded.

One of the control agency's next moves would
be to tackle the air pollution sources that can reduce their levels of pollutant emissions in fairly
straightforward ways that clearly yield benefits
greater than costs.   This might mean that the agency
should proceed against those polluters who are perceived by both the control agency and the public at
large as the most significant polluters of the atmosphere in the jurisdiction--but not always.   For
example, it is now recognized by New York City officials concerned with air pollution that the
formulators of Local Law 14 made an error in the
structuring of the legislation by requiring that
initial action be taken against on-site incinerators, even though they were a source of easily visible localized particulate concentrations.

Initial agency action, in addition to avoiding
potential charges of being "arbitrary and capricious," must consider the impact of highly localized
costs in relation to diffuse benefits and whether

the technological and administrative solutions to
problems are at hand. It is now argued by New York
City Air Pollution Control officials that a much
greater reduction of air pollution could have been
achieved at a lower cost to individual polluters
by proceeding initially against the emissions of
sulfur oxides and particulates resulting from the
burning of fuel oil. A technical solution--switching
to low-sulfur fuel oil--was available and could be
implemented without too much difficulty.* In fact,
due to difficulties involved in getting thousands of
on-site incinerators upgraded or shut down, the program to change to a low-sulfur fuel, which was initiated after the incinerator upgrading, yielded tangible benefits much sooner.

Selecting the initial target in this manner has
considerable implications in terms of later control
efforts. A demonstrated success gives the agency
a good image, reflects positively on the elected
officials who give the agency support, and lessens
the opposition of businessmen to control efforts
aimed at them. The stage is also set for conflict
resolution procedures such as negotiation rather
than for the polarization of attitudes that results
in litigation. These negotiations will in large
part deal with questions of uncertainty.

Structuring a Program to
Deal with Uncertainty

Air quality management programs in the United
States are faced with the necessity of ad hoc
regulation of individual industrial polluters who
have not had to comply with air pollution abatement
regulations in the past and who often view such
regulations as either too stringent or unnecessary.
The two case studies have shown that the adoption
of air pollution abatement regulations does not
invariably lead to pollution abatement.[2] Protecting

---

*Although making the use of low-sulfur fuel man-
datory is in conflict with the economist's preference
for giving the polluter flexibility of response, it
can still be viewed as a sound decision in keeping
with our strategy, which would allow mixing of
necessary approaches. At a later stage, another
approach should probably be substituted.

the regulations from legal attack and facilitating--
and in some cases forcing--compliance with such
regulations has been shown to be a critical part of
an air quality management program. In such a decision environment, major emphasis needs to be given
to the reduction of the psychological opposition to
regulation and the development of channels of communication between the emitter of pollution and the
control agency. Such emphasis, as noted earlier,
would have the aim of bringing unforeseen costs into
the open and, more generally, specifying the many
aspects of the uncertainty constraint.

As local air pollution control ordinances and
statutes are now formulated, ad hoc bargaining as
a formal device is ruled out, although practice
almost inevitably opens some opportunities for give
and take between polluters and the control agency
in both standard-setting and compliance stages.
But, as noted earlier, in passing the Air Quality
Act of 1967, Congress apparently contemplated that
new state legislation would be forthcoming, and this
expectation coupled with a fairly clear congressional
mandate that pollution control be undertaken selectively in light of technological feasibility,* suggests that new thought should be given to devising
machinery that will be capable of controlling pollution most effectively. Indeed, if the concepts of
"technological and economic feasibility" are equated
with benefit-cost analysis, the question arises
whether some existing regulatory schemes might fail
to meet the approval of the Department of Health,
Education and Welfare. The issue that is raised is
whether the federal act would justify Department
disapproval of state legislation on the ground of
heavy-handedness, or lack of willingness to dis-
criminate among polluters on the basis of the many
economic and administrative factors contained in
an optimal, least-cost solution that attempts to
cope with uncertainty. The act suggests, however,
that review is limited to assuring only that maximum

---

*Section 107 (c) provides, "Such recommendations
shall include such data as are available on the latest
technology and economic feasibility of alternative
methods of prevention and control of air contamination
including cost-effectiveness analysis."

effectiveness is achieved,* and the Department
may be motivated to define effectiveness so as to
review only for weakness and not for potential economic hardship on polluters.

The remainder of this chapter, drawing on these
suppositions, sets forth some ideas about the shape
and function of air quality management programs
that can best approximate least-cost solutions within the specified constraints. As noted earlier,
the outlook is for programs of direct regulations
rather than for the effluent fees approach advocated
by the welfare economist. Although the data shortages that prevent implementation of effluent fees
will also plague programs of direct regulation, the
latter approach is more familiar and could probably
sustain a greater amount of regulation in relative
ignorance than could a more novel system. In keeping with the "new federalism," which is often
praised as lending itself to experimentation and
innovation in ways of attacking particular problems,
the Department of Health, Education and Welfare
should not, in exercising its supervisory powers,
restrict states and their subdivisions to traditional patterns of regulation. Indeed, the regional
approach to regulation specified by the Air Quality
Act would seem to anticipate and encourage new departures. Such innovation and experimentation at
the regional level might produce significantly improved regulatory procedures. The following proposal is an innovative one that aims at avoiding
the specific problems documented in this study.

―――――――――――

*The state control plan will be approved if the
Secretary finds, among other things, "that such State
standards are consistent with the air quality criteria and recommended control techniques issued pursuant to section 107." As noted, Section 107 (c)
provides that control techniques should be based on
technological and economic feasibility. But the
state enforcement plan need only be "consistent with
the standards of air quality within a reasonable
time," and must provide "a means of enforcement by
State action, including authority comparable to" certain emergency powers provided in the act [Section
108 (c) (i)]. Thus, the emphasis arguably is on
achieving prompt compliance and not on cost effectiveness.

The Organizing Principle

In future attempts at air quality management,
primary consideration needs to be given to the central difficulty of legislating and regulating with
seriously imperfect scientific understanding and
within the constraints of inadequate but fast-
changing technology. Whereas air quality management
will continue to give major emphasis to direct regulation, the approach outlined in the following discussion is one most common in other systems of such
regulation and reflects the regional emphasis found
in the Air Quality Act of 1967. It features an independent regulatory body (the "commission") supported by a staff of legal and technical experts;
the commission's jurisdication could be metropolitan,
area-wide or even multistate in nature. Membership
on the commission would be for a relatively long
fixed term, and, because of the nature of the issues
to be encountered, the members might be required to
have expertise of specified types. Thus, the commission would be composed of lawyers, economists,
pollution control engineers, health specialists, and
other professionals. (A. J. Benline, the Commissioner of the Department of Air Pollution Control
in New York City during the period just preceding
that covered in the case study, attributes much of
the deficiencies in the New York City program to
the fact that professional engineers had insufficient
influence in the formulation of Local Law 14.[3]) The
commission would operate as an independent decision-
maker, and its final rulings would be subject to
judicial review. The agency staff would bear the
major enforcement burden and would provide the evidence and expertise guiding the commission's efforts.

It is increasingly held today that pollution
of the environment must be treated as a crime and
handled as a matter of litigation. The proposal
here described, on the other hand, holds that any
attempt to hypothesize about the outlines of an
enforcement program that attempts to approach a
least-cost solution through administrative means
must recognize the desirability of avoiding the
use of litigation before either judicial or administrative tribunals as the primary means of achieving
abatement in individual cases. The limitations of
both legal and technical staff resources, the difficulty of resolving highly uncertain technical

issues in an adversary proceeding, and the considerable administrative costs involved all point to the need for minimizing the use of litigation wherever possible.[4] The approach most helpful in achieving this objective would be to structure regulation to encourage the use of what has been defined as bargaining behavior backed by clearly defined legal authority as the primary means of accomplishing regulatory objectives. Such a structuring would include the following conditions:

(1) The management agency's regulations should provide for establishment of either informal or formal communication with both actual and potential polluters. Although this practice can lead to excess bureaucracy and paper work, it would be extremely helpful to avoid adversary positions and confrontations. Thus, it might be required that all polluters within the agency's jurisdiction file reports with the agency on their present emission levels and perhaps a ten-year estimate of anticipated increases or decreases in these emissions. Such information is critical for the development of an emissions inventory and an air quality management plan, yet a great majority of air pollution agencies in this county have inadequate emission data. Other continuing contact would also be desirable, and informal conferences could be called that would bring the agency staff, trade associations, representatives of local jurisdictions, the affected states, the metropolitan planning agency, and other interest groups together to discuss local problems. The author's interviews with Los Angeles Air Pollution Control District personnel confirm that informal conferences have been a key element in successfully controlling stationary sources of pollution.

(2) The agency's potential sanctions must be substantial but flexible enough so that they could be adjusted to the nature and magnitude of each particular problem confronted. Massive fines for emitting a small amount of pollution, for example, would be a poor agency strategy in that it

would distort the credibility of the agency's image as an arbiter of the public interest.

(3) The sanctions must put no premium on delay. Thus, a retroactive effluent charge, perhaps accumulating from the date of the agency's complaint, might be provided as a means of compelling a polluter to negotiate means to reduce his emissions with the management agency. Filing of a complaint would likely lead to a serious search for least-cost abatement techniques before a formal proceeding was initiated, much as the Federal Power Commission and the Federal Communications Commission have tended to negotiate rate reductions without starting a formal rate case.[5] With this strategy, conflict resolution would also be encouraged after a complaint was filed.

(4) The management agency's regulations must have the support of elected officials within the agency's jurisdiction and a strong legislative mandate to abate pollution. Although regulatory agencies are typically too weak rather then too strong and the agency's sanctions must be strong enough to encourage polluters to engage in pollution abatement in good faith, they should also not be so strong as to allow the agency to enforce its will without some recourse for the polluter. This surprising condition--that weaker sanctions may be desirable in some cases--is dictated by the conclusion of studies of mixed conflict and cooperation situations that the "game" will not be constituted in good faith unless each side has something to win and something to lose, and that both must be in a position to lose if an outcome is not achieved in the formal decision-making process. The final sanction of formal proceedings against the polluter therefore should be costly to both the agency and the polluter because it is such an inefficient and time-consuming method of pollution abatement. In an environmental management situation such as this where

there is a great deal of uncertainty, the
cost implications of abatement strategies
need to be considered in detail and aired
publicly if something approximating the
optimal, least-cost solution is to be
arrived at. Stringent regulations developed without considering the polluter's
potential reaction and giving little attention to the magnitude and distribution
of abatement costs will result at best in
a high-cost solution and at worst in a lack
of compliance on a large scale. Firms
faced with stringent regulations who wish
to search for least-cost solutions may find
that authoritarian regulatory agency decisions discourage such a search.

(5) If informed bargaining is to operate to
the public's advantage, the agency must be
adequately staffed so that it is known that
its sanctions will not go uninvoked if
agreement is not reached or if bargaining
is not conducted in good faith. The abatement of 90 per cent of the emissions from
stationary sources of air pollution in Los
Angeles County, for example, was achieved
in part through the efforts of several
hundred Air Pollution District employees.
The New York experience recited above also
illustrates the importance of credibility
of sanctions.

(6) Public utility regulation points to the
fact that the public's representatives at
the bargaining table must be neither al-
together free of nor unduly subject to political influence, in order, first, that
excessive zeal or laxness can be checked
and, second, that polluters may not accomp-
lish through influence what they are unable
to achieve by negotiation.[6]

(7) Experience with other types of regulation
also suggests the desirability of maintaining public control of administrative discretion through openness in decision-making.
Thus, the data submitted by both the
polluter and the agency staff, the terms
of the settlement itself, the staff's

reasons for accepting it, and the commission's approval should be on public file.* Also useful might be annual or more frequent reports of settlements, together with underlying data, which could be used by the legislative bodies to which the agency is responsible.[7] Public disclosure avoids potential charges that the agency has made "deals" not in the public interest and establishes a reputation value for the agency's decisions that is useful in future negotiations with polluters. It should be noted that this requirement of public disclosure would not allow the secrecy often said to be necessary for delicate negotiations. Even though there is probably some validity to this assertion, in air quality management, where considerable public support is essential for effective pollution abatement, the "glare of publicity" is one of the more effective devices an agency has and should not be given up for possibly lesser benefits derived from secrecy.

(8) A final precondition for effective air quality management is a clearly defined legal framework within which conflict resolution procedures can operate. This is essential so that the participants--the agency staff and the polluter--can largely avoid differences on questions of legal principle while concentrating on the development of the technical and economic data needed to reach a judgment and about potential least-cost solutions.** Included among

---

*Section 108 (c) (5) of the Air Quality Act of 1967 states, in connection with hearings conducted under the act, "no witness or any other person shall be required to divulge trade secrets or secret processes." Such confidentiality must be provided by any regulatory scheme.

**Testimony on the importance of establishing such a framework appears in an opinion of the Federal Communications Commission defending the decision to commence the first full-scale rate case against AT&T. In response to Bell Telephone's stated perference

the many issues that ideally need to be
classified so that they can be largely
eliminated from dealings with polluters
are as many of the over-riding facts as
possible about the air pollution problem
in the particular air-shed. Such questions
as estimates of pollution damage in general
and attribution of this damage to particular pollutants or groups of pollutants
would be best resolved authoritatively
after agency data gathering and research
and public hearings open to all interested
parties. Negotiations and conferences with
polluters could hopefully then proceed
without calling these basic matters into
question. If conditions such as the foregoing could be created, face-to-face negotiations and conferences could be made to
serve an important function. It is argued
that the advantages would be many, including establishment of cooperative attitudes
between regulators and industry, which
would encourage a joint search for solutions to problems; a de-emphasis of fact-
finding through quasi-judicial processes
and the avoidance of excessive reliance
on "experts" with opposite views, which is
characteristic of adversary proceedings
requiring expert testimony; speed, flexibility, and efficiency in the sense that
appellate proceedings and time-consuming
judicial review would be avoided; and a
more efficient use of technical, administrative, and legal staffs.

TOWARD A LEAST-COST SOLUTION

There is an axiom among engineers that one
can "go slow by running too fast." Although this

---

for negotiation as a rate-making method, the Commission stated, "Indeed, we believe that the standards
and criteria developed on the record here will enable us to employ continuing surveillance (i.e.,
negotiation) even more effectively in the future."
American Telephone and Telegraph Co., 61 P.U.R. 3rd,
1960, pp. 559-60.

statement can be interpreted by control officials
with some justification as a polluter's excuse for
doing nothing, the establishment of the precondi-
tions for an effective control program is a case
where the axiom applies. The structuring of the
process that will produce efficient resource allocation depends in large part, as has been noted, on
the decisions of the legislators who create the
sanctions and provide the enforcement staff and
on the establishment of a clear legal and factual
framework within which to operate. Whereas a prime
objective is to keep as many issues as possible out
of litigation, the agency needs the authority to
negotiate concerning factual uncertainty. Given
the state of the art in environmental management,
the legislators need to realize that the "best
guess" approach requires that some substantial degree of discretion be given to the agency and its
technical staff.

The commission will begin developing the necessary factual framework by holding public hearings
as a prelude to authoritative findings on these
factual issues:

(1)   General estimates of the total damages at-
      tributable to air pollution in the air-
      shed.

(2)   The general allocation of these damages
      to each pollutant or each major group of
      sources. The findings on these first two
      points need not be sufficiently detailed
      to satisfy a welfare economist, and it
      is obvious that the goal is simply the
      best estimates possible.

(3)   An inventory of emissions, including the
      total amount of each pollutant emitted by
      point sources. A point source is defined
      by the National Air Pollution Control
      Administration as any stationary source
      for which actual emission data are avail-
      able. In some instances, due to time and
      personnel restrictions, it is necessary
      to limit data collecting and calculations
      to sources above a certain size. Generally
      speaking, a point source is considered to
      be any source that emits more than ten
      tons a year of any pollutant. If personnel

and time restrictions are a limiting factor, 100 tons a year can be used as a
cut-off point.

(4)   A knowledge of the specific location of
      area sources (below the cut-off point)
      and an agreed-upon figure indicating the
      level of background or environmental pol-
      lution. The latter figure reflects
      "natural" sources such as dust blown up
      by a strong wind.

(5)   The relationship of emission levels to the
      assimilative capacity of the ambient air.
      The National Air Pollution Control Admini-
      stration recommends the Martin-Tikvart
      diffusion model; its technical staff as-
      sists in the calibration of this relatively
      simple model to specific geographical
      areas.

(6)   The objectives of the abatement program,
      stated in terms of air quality and the
      level of residual damages anticipated as
      optimal for the air-shed as a whole.

Some of the foregoing factual judgments would
be based in part on the air quality criteria issued
by the Department of Health, Education and Welfare.[8]
Also available from the Department's National Air
Pollution Control Administration is a general bene-
fit/cost (econometric) model, a control strategy
model, and a cost model of control. With assistance,
these can be adapted to specific geographical areas.

The gathering of these data and the use of the
various simulation models being perfected allows
the air quality management agency to develop and
test a series of alternative strategies of pollution
abatement. For example, one could test the viability
of a maximum control technology strategy versus an
existing standards strategy. These models thus provide extremely useful data for developing the factual
framework. They are not, however, an end in themselves but a series of tools that augment existing
management techniques.

Because air pollution must be considered in a
systems context with water pollution and solid wastes

disposal, these data should not be compiled in
isolation from plans and programs for dealing with
environmental quality problems developed by other
functional agencies. Data from a metropolitan or
area-wide planning agency would be a logical source
of information on relationships such as these. Additional evidence would be required, and the agency's
conclusions should be buttressed by subsidiary findings and a reasoned opinion. All such findings
would be subject to periodic review and revision,
each time following the procedures employed in the
initial formulation. Taken together, these findings
should give a sufficiently clear picture to allow
the decision-making framework to begin functioning.

A matter the agency would find appropriate to
resolve in a rule-making proceeding is the development of a generalized technique for determining a
polluter's contribution to the region's over-all
concentration of pollutants--see (2) above. Once
this issue was settled in principle, the questions
at issue with each polluter would be (1) his re-
spective contribution of pollutants to concentrations in the ambient air, which would probably be
fairly close to the proportion of total emissions
for which he was responsible, adjusted for such factors as wind, timing of emissions, and stack height
and (2) the polluter's costs associated with varying levels of abatement.

Ideally, the agency staff would be able to
negotiate effectively within this framework of
settled legal and economic principles and authoritative general findings of fact concerning the extent
and danger of pollution. The issues at stake in
the negotiations with polluters would be almost
exclusively factual and would be susceptible to
quantified solutions, thus facilitating some compromise in areas of valid doubt. Focal point
bottlenecks could be largely avoided in that matters of legal and economic principle would have
been eliminated for the most part by rule-making;
where legal questions did arise, they could be set
aside for separate authoritative decision by the
commission. Such procedures would allow time for
incrementalism to operate to narrow gradually the
range of possible results, and the continuing negotiating machinery, which would be focused primarily

on technical issues, would provide a hospitable
climate for the resolution of these issues.*

One of the more important matters that should
concern a control agency operating under this system is the establishment of a method of determining
the maximum abatement expenditure--or level of abate-
ment--that could be required of polluters. This
complex question has practical importance because
all polluters cannot be attacked at once and the
marginal unit abatement costs apparently justified
when pollution levels are high will seem inappro-
priate if and when more nearly tolerable concentrations have been achieved.** A very rough figure
can be derived if air quality standards--indicators
of the level of air quality desired within a given
jurisdiction--have been developed from objectives
and constraints specified in the legislative process and in the air quality criteria of the Department of Health, Education and Welfare. Beginning
with these goals, which will necessarily include

---

*One of the reasons given for the success of
the Los Angeles Air Pollution Control District is
that there has been a great deal of cooperation between the technical staff of the District and the
technical staffs of the regulated industries.

**Because the aggregate cost curve for damage
abatement within an air-shed is almost certainly
non-linear--costs increase as the more obvious
sources of pollution are controlled and as the more
serious damage is eliminated--an estimate of the
amount of damage reduction obtainable from a unit
of abatement by the first polluter proceeded against
might be high if this polluter was considered as an
isolated source. This would apparently justify
imposition of equally high abatement costs. Such a
view of marginal control expenditures and benefits
is deceptive, however, in that if other firms or
groups of firms were forced to abate sequentially,
their positions on the curve would lower and their
expenditures would yield a lower return, thereby
decreasing the amount of required investment. Thus,
a simplistic comparison of marginal costs and benefits is not enough, for this would result in applying a different standard to each polluter depending
on the sequence in which they are attacked.

estimates of the abatement outlays required to
achieve them,* the agency can arrive at a general
estimate of the theoretical emission level at which
all marginal expenditures would equal marginal benefits. No polluter should be required to abate to
below that emission level which he would be permitted to maintain under such optimal conditions.

This does not mean to imply, however, that
polluters operating old and obsolete plants that
would be noncompetitive if forced to comply with
pollution abatement regulations would not be forced
to cease operation. In such a case where localized
abatement costs would be prohibitive but benefits
from such abatement large, two strategies are possible. First, the control agency could force the
polluter to reduce his emissions, thereby causing
him to cease operations. Second, in situations
where there is a question of "taking without just
compensation" which might result in a variance being
granted, the control agency could require polluters
to pay for the variances they seek, the fee to be
set in accordance with damage estimates. If variances were purchased rather than granted, they
could be used as a tool for minimum-cost pollution
abatement rather than as an escape clause to avoid
control. They would thus become more palatable to
the public and the control agency.**

----

*H. Thomas points out that to set a quality
criterion is to imput a benefit-cost ratio. Thus,
the starting point for pollution abatement programs
should be benefit-cost analysis and not arbitrarily
determined quality criteria or emission standards.
See H. Thomas, "The Animal Farm: A Mathematical
Model for the Discussion of Social Standards for
the Control of the Environment," Quarterly Journal
of Economics, LXXVII (February, 1963), 147.

**A variant of this proposal is the suggestion
by Charles Haar that airports lease the right to
make noise for a stated period of time from property
owners in adjacent areas. This would be an alternative to a permanent right to make noise at a level
prevailing at the time of a condemnation proceeding.
At the expiration of the lease period, the property
owner would be required to prove loss in value suffered due to noise. By settling claims at the expiration of the period, he suggests it would be

THE POLITICAL AND INSTITUTIONAL ENVIRONMENT

The two case studies clearly point to the fact that the environment in which air quality management decisions are made needs to be viewed from several different perspectives. It is useful to think of the "basic decision environment" of which the political and institutional framework is only part. Also pertinent is the legal basis for air pollution control, the seriousness of perception of the air pollution problem by the public and its elected representatives, and the history or past behavior of the major actors involved such as the air pollution control agency, public utilities, and specific industrial groups.

The basic decision environment needs to be related to the "issue environment." The issue might be control of either a specific type of air pollution such as sulfur dioxide or particulates or a specific type of source such as refinery or municipal incinerator emissions. The aspects of the issue environment can be listed as follows:

(1) the nature of the issue involved, e.g., control of particulates or sulfur dioxide in the air, or, alternatively, emissions from incinerators or electric power generating plants;

(2) the relation of the issue to the basic decision environment defined above;

---

easier to determine accurately the amount of damage by taking into account changes in noise levels that might have occurred. The advantages of such an approach are listed as the following: (1) All owners harmed by noise would be compensated. (2) The cost factor would lead to the proper location of airports where lease costs would be lowest. (3) The time-limited nature of the leasehold would encourage the air industry to develop quieter engines because the costs of making noise would be passed on to the airlines by the airports in the form of higher rents. See C. Haar, "Airport Noise and the Urban Dweller: A Proposed Solution" (Paper read before the Practicing Law Institute Urban Renewal Seminar, New York City, May 10, 1968).

(3) the nature of and uncertainties involved with the relevant technology;

(4) the issue actors as opposed to the basic actors;

(5) the methods for allocating abatement costs;

(6) the time constraints externally or internally imposed on decision-making.

This breakdown is helpful; air pollution as an issue itself is typically too broad a topic. Considerably different technological, economic, and political considerations are involved in the control of different types of sources and/or pollutants. For example, abatement of pollution from automobiles and that of pollution from on-site incinerators are quite dissimilar problems. These differences need to be reflected in the organizational approach to air quality management.

The organizational structure also needs to reflect the fact that air quality management is more than just air pollution abatement. Freeways, mass transit, solid waste disposal, and the location of industrial and residential areas all have an effect on air pollution. A management program that is to provide maximum utilization of the air for all parties requires a large degree of coordination of all land-use planning, zoning, public facility programming, and much other activity in the typical urban or metropolitan area. But, even though air pollution is most critical in metropolitan areas, nowhere in the Air Quality Act of 1967 is there any explicit recognition of existing regional governmental organizations such as a metropolitan planning agency or council of governments.* Thus, the Act's allocation of control responsibility--subject

---

*The Department of Health, Education and Welfare does not demand that applicants for clean air grants clear their application through recognized councils of governments. Where an effective council of governments exists in a region, applicants for air pollution control grants should be required first to submit those applications to the local government coordinating body, in order to determine whether or not the program objectives can be integrated into a

to federal oversight--to "air quality regions" transcending municipal and state boundaries raises questions of the relationship between the affected states that are to administer a coordinated program and existing metropolitan planning agencies and air pollution control programs. The problems raised and the solutions proposed in this study reveal that institutional organization is an issue that needs considerable attention in the future. No specific proposal is made here for a detailed institutional format for air quality management. However, it should be clear that the necessary regional approach that is developing must not exist independent of local governmental units which will feel the pressure of polluters forced to abate their emissions.

CONCLUSION

Viewed as an entity, the most telling criticism of this study must be that the procedures suggested have not been shown to be viable based on actual experience in air quality management. Indeed, very little actual bargaining was observed. Much of the conclusions, therefore, are based on the broader definition of bargaining behavior. It can be argued, however, that the lack of suitable reference points for constructing such a decision framework as that presented here is due more to the sheer lack of experience in air quality management than to the inapplicability of the framework to the problem. This assertion is borne out by the much greater volume of experience in water pollution control, where bargaining over the setting of water quality standards is not uncommon.[9] Although a direct transfer of experience from water pollution to air pollution is perhaps not entirely valid, the author believes that the standard-setting process in environmental management needs to give due consideration to different perspectives and the state of incomplete knowledge.

---

comprehensive air management program for the air basin. Instead, the Air Quality Act gives an appointee of the governor the authority to recommend or deny approval of a grant. See J. O'Fallon, "Deficiencies in the Air Quality Act of 1967," Journal of Law and Contemporary Problems, XXXIII (Spring, 1968), 275.

In dealing with environmental quality problems, optimizing methods are a guide to decisions, not a philosopher's stone that substitutes for decision. With a view to achieving practical results, it has been pointed out how conflict resolution principles might contribute to finding a least-cost solution in air quality management. Although pro forma bargaining is often viewed as a distributional device rather than one that promotes efficiency, it has been shown that the latter view can also be taken when bargaining behavior is considered. Having been directed, or having found it expedient, to work toward a least-cost approach, the pollution control agency should be responsive within our framework to polluters' arguments based on a comparison of marginal benefits and costs associated with alternative emission reduction techniques. The polluter would most likely be inclined to search for the lowest-cost remedy and to develop and advance in the negotiations alternative ways of accomplishing the objectives being sought--an advantage, it will be recalled, usually associated exclusively with effluent fees as a control mechanism. Market forces will thus aid the controllers in seeking the most efficient approach to pollution damage reduction. For these reasons, the outcome of a properly structured planning process emphasizing bargaining principles should not deviate too far from economic rationality.

The hypothetical regulatory program we have outlined probably represents an ideal difficult to achieve in our society today. Why it may be so is a matter for conjecture and concern, and the most pessimistic conclusions one might draw is that the law and the legal system are in many respects incompatible with the scientific pursuit of optimal conditions under constraints of uncertainty.[10] We have proposed a scientific approach to pollution control requiring gross estimates of pollution damage and abatement costs. A problem of concern in this framework is the difficulty of making damage and cost estimates with enough objective validity to withstand legal attack when viewed as the product of a hearing record which must contain "substantial evidence" to support the result reached. In many respects, informed guesses will be all that a regulatory agency can show, and honesty should compel the agency to admit the depth of human ignorance on the questions at issue and to acknowledge frankly that its findings are made for the purpose

of getting on with the abatement job. The courts,
which traditionally have the role of providing
equity and justice for the polluter who has been
unfairly dealt with by a regulatory agency, would
then be faced clearly with the problem of allowing
regulation to proceed in the dim light of partial
knowledge or to cease until science can provide
light enough to satisfy the judicial sense of what
due process requires.

Experience with the public utility regulatory
process suggests, however, that agencies do not as a
rule confess ignorance but rather pretend to omnis-
cience. While often not disclosing the true basis
for their decisions and allowing their opinions to
be written in judge-proof "boiler-plate" by their
legal staffs, the agencies assume an air of know-
ledgability that belies more than it reveals. This
attitude might work in air pollution control as well,
as the early Federal Power Commission decision on
natural gas for Los Angeles indicates, and the
temptation to adopt it will be great. Control com-
missions may prefer to fill their opinions with
statistics and data and to conclude by solemnly declaring, "Having considered all of the evidence and
the relevant legal principles . . . ." The results
may be unimpeachable for the simple reason that the
underlying principles relating such items as costs
to benefits are not stated and thus are not subject
to review. The alternative may be unattractive in
administrative circles because the necessary estimates are of such precariousness that they can be
defended only by candor about the depth of the problem and by apparent conscientiousness in approaching it. Nevertheless, the courts, which play such
an important role in environmental quality control,
should learn to insist on full disclosure in lieu
of obfuscation. Once this is obtained, judicial
review should then require only the exercise of the
agency's expert judgment on the best information
and data available, incomplete and unsatisfying as
it may seem. In no event should the courts prevent
effective regulatory action solely because science
has not yet yielded the secrets needed to realize
the regulatory ideal.

NOTES

1. This information was derived from interviews with Maynard Hufschmidt, Professor of City and Regional Planning, University of North Carolina, and Blair Bower of Resources for the Future, Washington, D.C.

2. M. Holden notes a similar experience in state water pollution control. See M. Holden, Pollution Control as a Bargaining Process: An Essay on Regulatory Decision-Making (Ithaca, N.Y.: Cornell University Water Resources Center, 1966).

3. A.J. Benline, "Air Pollution--Metropolitan New York Area," The Municipal Engineers Journal, LIV (1968), 33-42.

4. The inadequacies of a litigation-oriented approach are detailed in Waste Management and Control, Pub. No. 1400 (Washington, D.C.: National Academy of Sciences, National Research Council, 1966), pp. 203-21.

5. See L. Welch, "Constant Surveillance: A Modern Regulatory Tool," Villanova Law Review, VII (1963), 340.

6. For experience in this area, see ibid.

7. Evaluation of agency performance by the legislature is one of the more important aspects of a rational decision process. A. Maass et al., Design of Water Resource Systems (Cambridge: Harvard University Press, 1962), Ch. 15.

8. See the following publications of the Department of Health, Education and Welfare, National Air Pollution Control Administration: Guidelines for the Development of Air Quality Standards and Implementation Plans, May, 1969; Air Quality Criteria for Particulate Matter, January, 1969; Air Quality Criteria for Sulfur Oxides, January, 1969.

9. For a more optimistic view, see Waste Management and Control, op. cit., pp. 204-9, 214-17.

10. See Holden, op. cit.; A. Kneese and B. Bower, Managing Water Quality (Baltimore: The Johns Hopkins Press, 1968), pp. 224-35.

BIBLIOGRAPHY

BIBLIOGRAPHY

Books

Anderson, J. Politics and the Economy. Boston: Little, Brown, 1966.

Boulding, K. Conflict and Defense: A General Theory. New York: Harper, 1962.

_____. The Impact of the Social Sciences. New Brunswick, N.J.: Rutgers University Press, 1966.

Braybrooke, D., and Lindbloom, C. A Strategy for Decision. New York: Free Press, 1964.

Bruner, J., et al. A Study of Thinking. New York: John Wiley & Sons, 1957.

Buchanan, J., and Tullock, G. The Calculus of Consent. Ann Arbor: University of Michigan Press, 1962.

Charlesworth, J. (ed.). Contemporary Political Analysis. New York: Free Press, 1967.

Churchman, R., Ackoff, R., and Arnoff, E. Introduction to Operations Research, New York: John Wiley & Sons, 1957.

Ciriacy-Wantrup, S. Resource Conservation: Economics and Policies. Rev. ed., Berkeley: University of California Division of Agriculture Sciences, 1963.

Cyert, R., and March, J. A Behavioral Theory of the Firm. Englewood Cliffs, N.J.: Prentice-Hall, 1967.

Diesing, P. Reason in Society. Urbana: University
     of Illinois Press, 1962.

Douglas, A. Industrial Peacemaking. New York:
     Columbia University Press, 1962.

Eckstein, O. Water Resources Development: The Eco-
     nomics of Project Evaluation. Cambridge:
     Harvard University Press, 1958.

Enthoven, A. "The Simple Mathematics of Maximiza-
     tion." An appendix in C. Hitch and R. McKean,
     The Economics of Defense in the Nuclear Age.
     Cambridge: Harvard University Press, 1960.

Herber, L. Crisis in Our Cities. Englewood Cliffs,
     N.J.: Prentice-Hall, 1965.

Herfindahl, O., and Kneese, A. Quality of the En-
     vironment. Baltimore: The Johns Hopkins
     Press, 1965.

Hirshleifer, J., et al. Water Supply: Economics,
     Technology and Policy. Chicago: University
     of Chicago Press, 1960.

Holden, M. Pollution Control as a Bargaining Process:
     An Essay on Regulatory Decision-Making.
     Ithaca, N.Y.: Cornell University Water Re-
     sources Center, 1966.

Kapp, W. The Social Costs of Private Enterprise.
     Cambridge: Harvard University Press, 1950;
     Rev. ed. 1963.

Kariel, H. The Decline of American Pluralism. Stan-
     ford, Calif.: Stanford University Press, 1961.

Kneese, A. The Economics of Regional Water Quality
     Management. Baltimore: The Johns Hopkins
     Press, 1964.
     _____, and Bower, B. Managing Water Quality.
     Baltimore: The Johns Hopkins Press, 1968.

Krutilla, J., and Eckstein, O. Multiple Purpose
     River Development. Baltimore: The Johns
     Hopkins Press, 1958.

Kuhn, H., and Tucker, A. (eds.). Contributions to
    the Theory of Games. Princeton, N.J.: Prince-
    ton University Press, 1954.

Little, I. M. D. A Critique of Welfare Economics.
    London: Oxford University Press, 1957.

Luce, R., and Raiffa, H. Games and Decisions. New
    York: John Wiley & Sons, 1957.

Maass, A., et al. Design of Water Resource Systems.
    Cambridge: Harvard University Press, 1962.

March, J., and Simon, H. Organizations. New York:
    John Wiley & Sons, 1958.

McKean, R. Efficiency in Government through Systems
    Analysis. New York: John Wiley & Sons, 1958.

Meyerson, M., and Banfield, E. Politics, Planning
    and the Public Interest. New York: Free
    Press, 1955.

Mishan, E. J. Welfare Economics: Five Introductory
    Essays. New York: Random House, 1964.

Olson, M. The Logic of Collective Action. New
    York: Schocken Books, 1968.

Pigou, A. The Economics of Welfare. London,
    Macmillan & Co., 1932.

Price, D. Science and Government. New York: New
    York University Press, 1954.

Rapoport, A. Fights, Games and Debates. Ann Arbor:
    University of Michigan Press, 1960.

_____. Prisoner's Dilemma. Ann Arbor: Univer-
    sity of Michigan Press, 1965.

Robbins, L. Politics and Economics: Papers in Po-
    litical Economy. New York: St. Martin's
    Press, 1963.

Schelling, T. The Strategy of Conflict. New York:
    Oxford University Press, 1963.

Shubik, M. Competition, Oligopoly, and the Theory of Games. Princeton, N.J.: Princeton University Press, 1958.

_____ (ed.). Game Theory and Related Approaches to Social Behavior. New York: John Wiley & Sons, 1964.

Simon, H. Administrative Behavior. New York: Free Press, 1965.

_____. Models of Man. New York: John Wiley & Sons, 1957.

Smith, A. R. Air Pollution. New York: Pergamon Press, 1966.

Stern, A. C. (ed.). Air Pollution. Vol. I. 2d ed.; New York: Academic Press, 1968.

Stevens, C. Strategy and Collective Bargaining Negotiation. New York: McGraw Hill, 1963.

Von Neumann, J., and Morgenstern, O. Theory of Games and Economic Behavior. New York: John Wiley Science Edition, 1967.

Waste Management and Control. Pub. No. 1400; Washington, D.C.: National Academy of Sciences, National Research Council, 1966.

Wolozin, H. (ed.). The Economics of Air Pollution. New York: W. W. Norton, 1966.

Articles and Periodicals

Anscombe, F., and Aumann, R. "A Definition of Subjective Probability," Annals of Mathematical Statistics, XXXIV (1963), 199-205.

Benline, A. J. "Air Pollution--Metropolitan New York Area," The Municipal Engineers Journal, LIV (1968), 33-42.

Boiteux, M. "Peakload Pricing," The Journal of Business, XXXIII (April, 1960), 157-79.

Bolan, R. "Emerging Views of Planning," Journal of the American Institute of Planners, XXXIII (July, 1967), 233-45.

Cohen, J.   "Interstate Compacts--An Evaluation,"
    Journal of the Air Pollution Control Associa-
    tion," XVII (October, 1967), 676-78.

Douglas, A.   "The Peaceful Settlement of Industrial
    and Intergroup Disputes," Journal of Conflict
    Resolution, I (March, 1957), 69-81.

Etzioni, E.   "Mixed Scanning: A Third Approach to
    Decision-Making," Public Administration Review,
    XXVII (December, 1967), 385-92.

Hanks, J., and Kuble, H.   "Industry Action to Curb
    Pollution," Harvard Business Review, XLIV
    (September-October, 1966), 49-62.

Harsanyi, J.   "A General Theory of Rational Behavior
    in Game Situations," Econometrica, XXXIII
    (July, 1966), 613-34.

_____. "On the Rationality Postulates Under-
    lying the Theory of Cooperative Games," Jour-
    nal of Conflict Resolution, V (June, 1961),
    179-96.

Havemann, R.   "Comment," Quarterly Journal of Eco-
    nomics, LXXXI (November, 1967), 695-702.

Hirshleifer, J.   "Peak Loads and Efficient Pricing:
    Comment," Quarterly Journal of Economics,
    LXXII (August, 1958), 451-62.

Hufschmidt, M.   "Environmental Planning," American
    Behavioral Scientist, X (September, 1966),
    6-8.

_____. "Field Level Planning of Water Resource
    Systems," Water Resource Research, Vol. I,
    No. 2 (1965), 147-63.

Ikle, F., and Leites, N.   "Political Negotiation as
    a Process of Modifying Utilities," Journal of
    Conflict Resolution, VI (March, 1962), 19-28.

Kennedy, H.   "Legal Aspects of Air Pollution Con-
    trol," Public Health Reports, LXXIX (August,
    1964), 688-705.

Koo, A.   "Recurrent Objections to the Minimax Strat-
    egy," Review of Economics and Statistics, XLI
    (February, 1959), 36-43.

Maass, A. "Benefit-Cost Analysis--Its Relevance for
    Public Investment Decisions," Quarterly Journal
    of Economics, LXXX (May, 1966), 208-26.

Marglin, S. "The Social Rate of Discount and the
    Optimal Rate of Investment," Quarterly Journal
    of Economics, LXXVII (February, 1963), 99-106.

Martin, R., and Symington, L. "A Guide to the Air
    Quality Act of 1967," Journal of Law and Con-
    temporary Problems, XXX (Spring, 1968), 239-74.

Mazur, A. "A Nonrational Approach to Theories of
    Conflict and Coalitions," Journal of Conflict
    Resolution, XII (June, 1968), 176-205.

McKean, R. "The Unseen Hand in Government," Ameri-
    can Economic Review, LXXIX (June, 1965), 494-
    506.

Michelman, F. "Property, Utility, and Fairness:
    Comments on the Ethical Foundations of Just
    Compensation Law," Harvard Law Review, LXXX
    (March, 1967), 1165.

Pollack, L. "Legal Boundaries of Air Pollution
    Control--State and Local Legislative Purpose
    and Techniques," Journal of Law and Contempo-
    rary Problems, XXX (Spring, 1968), 331-54.

Randolph, L. "A Suggested Model of International
    Negotiation," Journal of Conflict Resolution,
    X (September, 1966), 344-53.

Schoeffler, S. "Towards a General Definition of
    Rational Action," Kyklos, VII (1954), 245-71.

Shklar, J. "Decisionism, " Nomos VIII: Rational
    Decision, ed. C. Friedrich. New York: Ather-
    ton Press, 1964, pp. 1-17.

Steiner, P. "Peak Loads and Efficient Pricing,"
    Quarterly Journal of Economics, LXXI (November,
    1957), 585-610.

Stern, A. C. "Basis for Criteria and Standards,"
    Journal of the Air Pollution Control Associa-
    tion, XV (June, 1965), 281-87.

_____. "Implications of the Air Quality Act of 1967," Transactions of the New York Academy of Science, XXX (April, 1968), 759-65.

_____. "Summary of Existing Air Pollution Standards," Journal of the Air Pollution Control Association, XIV (January, 1964), 5-14.

Stone, J. "An Experiment in Bargaining Games," Econometrica, XXVI (August, 1958), 286-96.

Summer, D. "Conflict, Compromise, and Belief Change in a Decision-Making Task," Journal of Conflict Resolution, XII (June, 1968), 215-21.

"Switching to Low Sulfur Oil: Con Ed's Story," Environmental Science and Technology, III (December, 1968), 1072-73.

Thomas, H. "The Animal Farm: A Mathematical Model for the Discussion of the Environment," Quarterly Journal of Economics, LXXXVII (February, 1963), 143-48.

Willis, R., and Joseph, M. "Prominence as a Predictor of the Outcome of Games of Agreement," Journal of Conflict Resolution, IV (June, 1959), 102-13.

Government Publications

Air Pollution Control District Act, California Health and Safety Code (West, 1967).

Illinois Revised Statutes, Chapter III 1/2.

New York City Charter, Rules and Regulations of Department of Air Pollution Control, Chapter 41, Administrative Code.

New York City Council Minutes, June 22, 1965, pp. 1185-1258.

New York Public Health Law. Section 1297 (McKinney 1966).

Proposed Practices for Economic Analysis of River Basin Projects. Report to the Federal Inter-Agency Committee on Water Resources by its

Subcommittee on Evaluation Standards, Washington, D.C., May, 1950.

"Steps Towards Cleaner Air," Congressional Record, Vol. III, No. 4. (January 7, 1965), p. 283.

U.S. Department of Health, Education and Welfare, Air Pollution Engineering Manual. (Public Health Service Publication 999-AP-40.) Washington, D.C.: Government Printing Office, 1968.

U.S. Department of Health, Education and Welfare, Air Quality Criteria for Particulate Matter. (Bureau of Disease Prevention and Environmental Control.) Washington, D.C.: Government Printing Office, January, 1969.

U.S. Department of Health, Education and Welfare, Air Quality Criteria for Sulfur Oxides. (Bureau of Disease Prevention and Environmental Control.) Washington, D.C.: Government Printing Office, January, 1969.

U.S. Department of Health, Education and Welfare, Automobile Air Pollution. (Second Report of the Secretary of Health, Education and Welfare to the U.S. Congress.) Washington, D.C.: Government Printing Office, July 15, 1955.

U.S. Department of Health, Education and Welfare, A Digest of State Air Pollution Laws. (Public Health Service Publication 711.) Washington, D.C.: Government Printing Office, 1966.

U.S. Department of Health, Education and Welfare, Proceedings, National Conference on Air Pollution, November 12-20, 1958. (Public Health Service Publication 654.) Washington, D.C.: Government Printing Office, 1959.

U.S. Department of Health, Education and Welfare, Proceedings, National Conference on Air Pollution, December 10-12, 1962. (Public Health Service Publication 1022.) Washington, D.C.: Government Printing Office, 1962.

U.S. Department of Health, Education and Welfare, Proceedings, National Conference on Air Pollution, December 12-14, 1966. (Public Health

Service Publication 1649.) Washington, D.C.:
Government Printing Office, 1966.

U.S. Department of Health, Education and Welfare,
     Progress in the Prevention and Control of Air
     Pollution, First Report of the Secretary of
     Health, Education and Welfare to the U.S. Con-
     gress. Washington, D.C.: Government Printing
     Office, June 28, 1968, pp. 15-28.

U.S. Department of Health, Education and Welfare,
     Today and Tomorrow in Air Pollution. (Public
     Health Service Publication 1555.) Washington,
     D.C.: Government Printing Office, n.d.

U.S. House of Representatives, The Adequacy of Tech-
     nology for Pollution Abatement. Report of the
     Research Management Advisory Panel through the
     Subcommittee on Science, Research and Develop-
     ment to the Committee on Science and Astro-
     nautics, 89th Cong., 2nd Sess., July 1, 1966.

U.S. House of Representatives, Air Pollution, 88th
     Cong., 1st Sess., House Report 508, 1963.

U.S. House of Representatives, Air Pollution Control
     86th Cong., 1st Sess., House Report 960, 1959.

U.S. House of Representatives, Air Pollution Control
     Progress Review, Hearings before the House
     Interstate and Foreign Commerce Committee.
     86th Cong., 2nd Sess., February 23, 24, 1960.

U.S. House of Representatives, Environmental Pollu-
     tion: A Challenge to Science and Technology.
     A report of the Subcommittee on Science, Re-
     search, and Development to the Committee on
     Science and Astronautics, 89th Cong., 2nd Sess.,
     October 1, 1966.

U.S. House of Representatives, Managing the Environ-
     ment. A report of the Subcommittee on Science,
     Research, and Development to the Committee on
     Science and Astronautics, 90th Cong., 2nd Sess.,
     June 17, 1968.

U.S. Senate, Air Pollution--1966. Hearings before
     a Subcommittee on Air and Water Pollution of
     the Committee on Public Works, 89th Cong., 2nd
     Sess., June 4, 7, 8, 14, 15, 1966.

U.S. Senate, Air Pollution--1967. Hearings before
the Subcommittee on Air and Water Pollution
of the Committee on Public Works, 90th Cong.,
1st Sess., February 13-May 18, 1967.

U.S. Senate, Air Pollution--1967, Part 3. Hearings
before the Subcommittee on Air and Water Pollution of the Committee on Public Works, 90th
Cong., 1st Sess., April and May, 1967.

U.S. Senate, Air Pollution Control, 88th Cong., 1st
Sess., Senate Report 638, 1963.

U.S. Senate, Air Quality Criteria, A Staff Report
of the Subcommittee on Air and Water Pollution,
Committee on Public Works, 90th Cong., 2nd
Sess., July, 1968.

U.S. Senate, Congressional White Paper on a National
Policy for the Environment. Submitted to Con-
gress under the auspices of the Committee on
Interior and Insular Affairs, U.S. Senate, and
the Committee on Science and Astronautics, U.S.
House of Representatives, 90th Cong., 2nd Sess.,
October, 1968.

U.S. Senate, A Study of Pollution--Air. Staff Report of the Committee on Public Works, 88th
Cong., 1st Sess., September, 1963.

Yaffe, C. "A Roll Call of the States--Where Do We
Stand in State and Interstate Air Pollution
Control," Proceedings, National Conference on
Air Pollution, Washington, D.C.: Government
Printing Office, 1966, pp. 359-63.

Newspapers

Los Angeles Examiner, November 14, 1958; May 12,
1959; July 8, 1960; March 17, 1961.

Los Angeles Herald, October 10, 1958.

Los Angeles Herald and Express, January 5, 1959.

Los Angeles Herald Examiner, January 3, 1962.

Los Angeles Mirror News, October, 20, 1959; June
27, 1959.

Los Angeles Times, April 8, 1959; December 2, 1959;
     June 24, 1959; March 5, 1961; December 12,
     1965.

Los Angeles Times Mirror, December 17, 1958.

New York Times, March 16, 1966; May 24, 1966; Decem-
     ber 10, 1966; February 21, 1967; May 1, 1967;
     May 12, 1967; May 15, 1967; May 16, 1967; May
     23, 1967; July 18, 1967; January 29, 1968;
     January 31, 1968.

Oil and Gas Journal, December 4, 1959.

Oil Daily, March 11, 1963; May 28, 1965.

Pacific Oil Marketer, June-July, 1960.

Pasadena Star News, July 9, 1960.

Westchester Citizen, January 31, 1963.

Western Oils, July 15, 1959.

Unpublished Material

"Air Pollution in New York City." Report of the
     Special Committee to Investigate Air Pollution
     of the New York City Council, Minutes of the
     City Council, June 22, 1965, pp. 1227-28.

"Ambient Air Quality Objectives--Classification
     System." New York State Department of Health,
     Board of Air Pollution Control, 1964.

"Criteria Used for Upgrading Existing Apartment
     House Incinerators in the City of New York."
     New York City Department of Air Pollution Con-
     trol, January, 1967.

Denny, H., and Limoges, E. "Summary of Our Memoran-
     dum--Public Law 14; Estimate of Impact Regard-
     ing Requiring Upgrading vs. Abandonment of
     Apartment House Incinerators." New York City
     Department of City Planning, December, 1966.

Freedom to Breathe. Report of the Mayor's Task
     Force on Air Pollution in the City of New York,
     June 20, 1966.

Fuller, L. J. "Air Pollution Control--A Billion
    Dollar Problem." Los Angeles Air Pollution
    Control District News Release, April 17, 1967.

Gerhardt, P. "Some Economic Aspects of Air Pollu-
    tion." Paper presented at the Mid-Atlantic
    States Section, Air Pollution Control Associa-
    tion Conference, October 4, 1967.

Heller, A. "Status Report on the On-Site Incinera-
    tor Program." New York City Department of Air
    Pollution Control, July 31, 1967.

Kennedy, H. "The History, Legal and Administrative
    Aspects of Air Pollution Control in the County
    of Los Angeles." Report submitted to the Board
    of Supervisors of the County of Los Angeles,
    May 9, 1954.

Marlow, S. "On-Site Incineration--The View of the
    Regulatory Air Pollution Control Agency." Paper
    presented before the New York City Department of
    Air Pollution Control Refuse Disposal Workshop,
    December 9, 1967.

Report. Los Angeles County Air Pollution Control
    District, October, 1957.

Rules and Regulations. Los Angeles County Air Pol-
    lution Control District, March 3, 1967.

"Rules for the Prevention and Control of Air Con-
    tamination and Air Pollution." New York State
    Department of Health, Board of Air Pollution
    Control, 1967.

Siegel, G. "The National Government Evolves into
    the Vehicle Emission Field." Unpublished Manu-
    script, Air Pollution Control Institute, Uni-
    versity of Southern California, June, 1967.

"Summary of Conference and Conclusions and Recom-
    mendations on Interstate Air Pollution--New
    York-New Jersey Metropolitan Area." U.S. Public
    Health Service, January, 1967.

Vickrey, W. "Theoretical and Practical Possibilities
    and Limitations of a Market Mechanism Approach
    to Air Pollution Control." Paper presented at
    the Air Pollution Control Association Conference,
    Cleveland, Ohio, June, 1967.

Williams, T. "Experience with the Clean Air Act."
     Paper presented at the Third Conference on Air
     Pollution Control at Purdue University, October
     27, 1964.

Wolozin, H. "Intransigent Economic Behavior in Air
     Pollution Control and Economic Decision." Paper
     presented at the Air Pollution Control Associa-
     tion Conference, Cleveland, Ohio, June 1967.

Working Committee on Economic Incentives, Federal
     Coordinating Committee on the Economic Impact
     of Pollution Control. Cost Sharing with Indus-
     try? Washington, D.C., December 1967.

ABOUT THE AUTHOR

George H. Hagevik is currently Assistant Professor of Urban Planning and Policy Development at Livingston College, Rutgers University, New Brunswick, New Jersey. He teaches and does research in the area of environmental quality, which includes air and water pollution, solid waste management, and noise control.

Dr. Hagevik studied at the University of Washington and the University of North Carolina at Chapel Hill and received his doctorate in city and regional planning at the latter institution. From 1965 to 1968, he was the recipient of a fellowship from the Environmental Health Training Program, which is funded by the U.S. Public Health Service.

He has contributed to various journals, including the Journal of Law and Contemporary Problems, the Journal of the American Institute of Planners, and the Hastings Law Journal.